Early Stages Press
New York

Early Stages Press
330 West 42nd Street
New York, New York 10036

First edition 2004

Edited by Amy Sultan
Designed by Carla Bauer Design
Cover photo by Chuck Levey
Poet photos by Amy Sultan
Photo of Roland Legiardi-Laura by Paul Whicheleo

Printed in the United States of America

ISBN 1285

THIS BOOK IS DEDICATED TO

CARLOS BRIGANTE

WHO SPITS FORTH WITH BRILLIANCE,

LOVE, WISDOM, AND HONESTY.

HE SINGS HIS OWN SONG OF SORROW,

DANCES HIS OWN DANCE OF LOGIC.

CARLITO, ALL THE REBELS OF THE HEIGHTS

DREAM A FUTURE FOR YOU.

INTRODUCTION TO
REBEL VOICES FROM THE HEIGHTS

About a year and a half ago my friend, Amy Sultan, convinced me that I needed to go back inside the public school system in order to refresh my insights about education in America. She was right. I've been visiting and studying schools and working on a documentary about the dysfunctional nature of the school system and what might be done about it and I needed to be viscerally reminded, needed to touch, smell, see, hear, and taste. I needed to teach.

"We're going to a little 'alternative' high school in the Bronx." She said. You'll be the Visiting Artist and we'll work with the students by having them write about their reactions to the plays we take them to see."

"Responsive Writing" she called it. And her organization, Early Stages, for the past 20 years, has been providing free theater tickets to tens of thousands of school children each year.

"It is a wonderful thing you do Amy, really," I said, "providing poor kids with the opportunity to experience theater. But I'm not interested in teaching 'responsive writing' It seems like only one small piece of the puzzle that literacy starved kids need. And I'm certainly not interested in traveling up to the Bronx each week." I'm afraid I had become quite a lazy Manhattan snob over the years.

She was insistent and she was willing to bribe me.

"I'll drive you up each week," this stated with a withering gaze that told me that my provincial elitism was utterly unacceptable. "You can design your own program if you think you can do better, and you'll work with one of the best teachers I have ever met." She said. "Plus you'll get paid!" Ah yes paid! In spite of my best efforts, the rent still came due each month in the East Village and the career of a documentary filmmaker is…well…often less than lucrative. I reluctantly agreed to consider her proposal subject to a visit to the school. I'll visit the place, I thought, invent a polite excuse, and dance gracefully away from an experience I don't really think I need to have. "The Bronx" I kept thinking, it is simply too far to go to confirm what I already knew: That our school system was indeed a terminal experience for all who partook.

We are in Amy's car, driving up the East River. I try to imagine this trip as a weekly ritual—traffic jams, endless, seemingly purposeless construction, Manhattan imperceptibly merging into the Bronx—the familiar becoming the strange…it didn't bode well. One saving grace however, was that Amy and I see the world in much the same way and we could make one another laugh hysterically. So the ride to the Bronx each week, if it happens, I think, will be made tolerable…we drive up the river in the early morning traffic, most of our travel companions, unwilling occupants of their own cars, would rather be somewhere else I am sure—their sour, used faces show little more than stress to the rest of the world. Do I want to be part of this parade of living suicides on a regular basis—I am so content down in the East Village, cut off from the angry, sad struggles most folks are forced to endure? As we chat I am getting a little nervous, remembering the knots-in-stomach feeling that all first days at school induce and then Amy points out over the river to our destination. "See, that dome, that's the school." Surely that is not the school, I think—What high school sports a dome like that? Sitting atop a hill, 'the Heights,' as they are called—is a beautiful, green, copper domed building, looking like some august observatory, or Coleridge's "stately pleasure-dome," or perhaps Fitzgerald's "fresh, green breast of the new world"—well maybe this wont be so horrific, if we get to hang out under that dome each week.

"The school is housed in a building on the old NYU campus, now Bronx Community College, you know this place?"

"Not really." Once again betraying my provincialism.

"It was where they filmed some of the exterior quad scenes for "A Beautiful Mind".

I am beginning to get a warm feeling about our possible venture as I imagine Jennifer Connolly wandering the paths where I might teach. As we cross the river and start winding our way up the hill, Amy tells me lots of things about the school and the teacher we'll be working with and the kids, but I don't really hear any of it— I have been calmed down and placed in a womb-like stupor by imagining that a monstrous telescope lives under that dome and that I will soon begin having tea with Jennifer Connolly and chatting about the latest galactic discovery.

We park the car just outside the campus, which is ringed with a tall black-iron fence, next to the school is a low-key military base, probably leftover from a time when the heights were strategic. It's surrounded by its own charming, razor wire fencing. I step out onto the narrow pathway that passes for a sidewalk and immediately into a steaming pile of fresh dog shit. Jennifer's pleasant visage melts away as the pungent odor of slippery reality takes hold. In fact I am surrounded by dog shit—I have to leap a good four feet to avoid more—Welcome to the Bronx.

"I guess this is where folks walk their dogs" Amy says.

I'm too busy trying to scrape, stomp, and dance the stuff off my shoes to reach over and try to strangle her. Note to self: Wear flat-soled shoes next time…if there is a next time.

We pass through the gates of the college—a security guard checks my ID but nothing else I am carrying, I guess the threat of terrorist attack here is considered minimal. At the far end of the campus is the former lab building that the Department of Education has captured from the College. Alas, it's not my dream dome but rather an undistinguished building neither modern nor old with a sort of crusty and slightly elegant institutional look to it from the outside. Amy proudly tells me that the students of the high school last year led a successful sit-down strike protesting the college's demand that metal detectors be installed in the school. Well, now it is easy to tell what message the kids are getting from the college and it is certainly not that of the welcoming open arms of an older brother eager to share in the adventure of learning. What could be the heart of the relationship between these two entities? Money perhaps? Certainly not one of mutual respect and support.

We enter the school building—more ID checking—because we are adults and perhaps because we are white there doesn't seem to be a lot of scrutiny—but this little indignity that we have all become so used to experiencing does not make the prospect of learning or teaching particularly enticing to anyone.

The principal, Brenda Bravo, greets us warmly. She has a heartening smile and relates to the students who freely wander in and out of her office with the confident air of a mother who knows best and who sincerely cares about her young charges.

"So tell me about the work you would like to do with our students...and please have a cookie and some tea if you like." I am sitting in a big comfortable chair in her office and my first inclination is to curl up and take a nap.

"Well, Brenda..." I opt for familiarity because I am an adult outside of her hierarchical world and I intend to keep it that way.

"...We're going to work on writing and reading and public speaking. I call the course a Power Writing Seminar. The goal is to empower the students with mastery of the culturally dominant English tongue." Once out of my mouth the words echo in the room for just a moment and I feel as if I have uttered some of the finest grade natural gas ever expelled. There is a silence and I expect Brenda to have both Amy and I escorted outside by security.

"Wonderful" she says. "You can start next week" Now I've done it, my prospects for escape have quickly narrowed.

We're taken on a brief tour of the school building—Two things stand out: There is a section of the school set up to care for infants and toddlers—the children of the children who attend. And in many of the rooms the walls don't go all the way up to the ceiling. I am heartened, saddened and angered by the 'maternity wing'. That the Dept. of Ed. and the city understand the situation that many of the students must adjust to in order scratch out an education is reassuring, but I am not so sure that school as an institution should take on the responsibility of childcare and I am angered that ultimately very little meaningful support is being offered to these youngest families. The walls and the ceilings were another matter entirely. The only message that was being sent here was that a quiet, respectful learning environment was not the priority of the system. How can you think if the hum and murmur of an entire building wafts over your head while you are supposed to be concentrating?

Walking into the classroom I'm surprised by several things—there aren't many students—perhaps 15 at most, I'm expecting a classic, overcrowded high school classroom. It is a science class—Why am I in a science class planning to teach writing? I'm encouraged though that the kids are focused and attentive. Amy introduces me to Joe, who acknowledges us but stays on track with his teaching. Watching Joe teach it becomes immediately apparent that he is anything but a typical teacher. After the class Joe, Amy and I talk—What impresses me about Joe is his devotion to the kids, his honesty, and his utter frustration with the school system. For the first time in this whole process I am engaged. Joe is someone I can learn from. We talk and plan, mostly Joe talks, telling us about the history of the school, what the kids are like and what he hopes to accomplish with a project like this. In listening to Joe you learn quickly that he comes from the same "street of blood" that his students now inhabit. I am feeling hopeful.

With Amy and Joe I am in a group of kindred spirits— the three of us have the same goal for the kids. We want to help them break out of the prison that has been constructed for them and that many of them are helping to maintain. It is essential that we see our work as coming from deep respect for the kids and not some arrogant post- colonial missionary notion that we're here to save them. And if this is going to work it is also essential that the three of us create some kind of safe coherent world for the kids in our classroom. Joe is a poet, a writer, a man who has lived. He knows who he is and he knows he wants to share his wisdom and experience with the kids. I leave our meeting, inspired and excited. Amy was right, there is a chance that something special could happen here.

For our first class meeting I come prepared with a complex, rich, extensive class curriculum. It is ambitious, looks out beyond the first year and would choke a Harvard graduate student. But that is my position. I expect these kids to work and I believe they are capable of anything Harvard kids can do and probably more. Amy and I purchase, elegant leather bound journals for each of the students—again the idea is simple, treat these youngsters seriously and respectfully and they will take on the work. Only about 10 students show up, it is an early morning class—beginning before regular school hours—officially we are called a 'club,' and the students have to choose between us and other enticing options like Dominoes.

My first speech to the students is straightforward:

"The prisons in our country house more people per capita than any other country in the world and they are filled with people who can't read or write or speak well. In fact this is the single most common distinguishing characteristic of an American prisoner—illiteracy. Not race, not economic background, not an abusive childhood. If you want to have power in this society you must master the three literacies and this is what we are going to focus on in our work. This is a class about power, your power, we're not going to teach anything that doesn't assist you in dealing effectively with the world around you and if we seem to wander or stray you are expected to call us on it." I'm proud of my little speech. I look around, no one says anything, but no one laughs, hurls anything or leaves the room.

And so it begins. We pass out the journals and start to write and to talk and to recite our work...all of us write...Joe and Amy and I as well...the classroom, it soon becomes clear, is a horrible place to work...There isn't enough time, it's noisy and the place reeks of the very things we are challenging the kids to abandon. Our first day of class there are 17 interruptions in a 40-minute period. Bells, and neighboring teachers walking in to borrow something, and staff stopping by with forms to fill out, and announcements...the message is clear— 'Your learning is the least important thing we are doing.' So we plot our escape—and Joe finds us a quiet, well-lit, grossly over-heated, seminar room across the quad at the college. And we start taking the kids on field trips to see films and plays and museums and we have work-days down at my loft—and the class stretches the time from one period to almost 3 hours of straight work and the kids don't flinch and they come regularly, even though their own lives are filled with unimaginable struggle and pain. And the number starts to grow. From seven regulars we now have as many as 25 crammed into our little seminar room. I am told it is the only class that some of them attend the entire week. I know we are doing something useful because even the kids who graduated from the school last year come back to work with us. And I am most proud when I hear that the Special Ed. Evaluator, after hearing our kids read their poetry, feels obliged to reevaluate their status.

They work hard each week, filling up their journals. Pearl is on her 4th journal, and her second novel, and Catalina has me help her glue her journal back together.

ROLAND LEGIARDI-LAURA

Yaritsa fills her journal with notes from our work at the Metropolitan Museum of Art. They all emboss the journal covers with their own art. Karina Sanchez starts each of her entries: "Dear God". In our class there are no bad kids and no stupid kids. Everyone has something important to share and they come back, week after week, to be heard. Perhaps for some of them it is the first time in their lives that people listen to them and respond with depth and passion. A culture develops in the class. It is one of support and gentle critique. After a year and a half I begin to think we have achieved something significant because the kids are working for themselves, not for me or Amy or Joe and they are helping each other and learning from each other. On any given day, if you were to visit our room, you might experience (in no particular) order the following:

—Alberto's brilliant, infectious, romantic poetry of passion and love.

—Chantay's bitter ironic humor, lusty rage and no-nonsense delivery that cross-fertilizes...

—Joel's Zen warrior wit and well defended cynicism.

—Charles' hilarious situation poetry, with deadpan delivery that ties everyone in knots.

—Syesha's powerful rhythm and titanic struggle now yielding a profound maturity.

—Pearl, who has become a hero, liberating the younger women in the class. Her own struggles have forged a powerful lyric voice. She has moved from pain and sadness to anger and action.

—Ron's complex ideas and tortured obsessive images, which challenge each of us to look inside.

—Jennifer, whose momentous breakthrough one morning, made everyone reach out to her, and we all became stronger for it.

—Jessica, Jennifer's fearless twin sister, doesn't officially attend University Heights but nevertheless comes to our class.

—Anthony's lurid sexuality and side ripping humor transformed before our very ears into the intense yearning of a young man bent on transcendence.

—Manny, who pushes the room with his passion and power.

—Ramon, a natural 'spitter' and shrewd analyst, delivers razor sharp political daggers, straight into the heart of our American social nightmare.

—Robbin, who tells the story of her childhood and shoves everyone who listens against the hard rock of reality.

—Dani, who caresses us with the music of her voice and then cuts through the air with images as infinite as the ocean.

—Karina S., who makes the room weep with her soft, assured voice and rich imagination.

—Kari C., who triumphantly straddles the delicate balance of two languages with grace.

—Yaritsa, a philosopher-poet, who tells us tales of distant galaxies and the inner universe.

—Maddy, who has conquered her shyness and now sports a clear-headed ferocity.

—Yasmine, who has the courage to cry into her poems.

—Adrien a master of the surreal who probes and bares, with wit and tenderness, his own soul.

—Catalina, who passed quickly from little girl to elegant wind-talker.

—The "New-Jacks" as Joe calls them: Aleva, Amanda, Arlene, Christina, Kenya, Matt and Maxine, all gleam with promise.

—Dorian, the master of smooth, thoughtful rap.

—Eli, who is firmly on the path of a spiritual searcher and whose poems have the rhythmic echoes of the best beat poetry.

—Johnny, a young man, on the edge, whose sporadic visits to our class are always welcome and wise.

—And Willie, who is a natural genius of sound, rhythm and meaning—makes you listen three times faster than you breathe...

...And the other students, who have occasionally drifted in and out of our room, not quite sure why they are there but sensing that something real might be happening, come briefly and share. Finally, there is Carlito— the ghost-demon of our class now, the banner of our struggle—someone whose spirit is revered and whose pure musical soul brought smiles all 'round.

These are the reasons I wake up each Friday morning smiling. At the end of a long class I should be exhausted and spent. Instead, Amy and I look at each other— refreshed, energized, glowing. We have been given the gift of spirit from these kids—warriors of the word, they are on a rampage through my heart and they take no prisoners.

It might be useful here to ruminate just a bit, as to why this little project seems to be successful, what its challenges are, and whether or not it has some larger value.

If we can legitimately claim success, the bulk of that success, I'm convinced, comes from doing some very simple things. Things that all good educators know:

■ Create a safe place for the students—a place where everyone feels it is ok to express oneself, to be vulnerable, without fear of ridicule or abuse.

■ Capture a quiet respectful room where the ethics of hard work, responsibility, and shared insight are honored. Not as easy as one might expect.

■ Build everyone's commitment through consistency. This means showing up without fail, following up with sincere interactions and doing what you say you are going to do.

■ Honesty—Gratuitous praise, rote criticism, and a line of smooth bull you don't really believe in, never pass muster with young people. They get it immediately and respond by disappearing literally or figuratively.

■ Listening—Everyone needs to feel they are being heard. Our kids have been profoundly short-changed in this regard.

■ Respect—this means that the "teachers" must be there to learn as well.

■ Warm support. This cannot be underestimated. If you don't feel happy about coming to this class as a student or teacher it can't work.

■ Empathy—if you can't feel at least a bit of other people's struggle, you're doomed to little more than condescension.

- Literacy is taught as a weapon—The work of the seminar is about survival, and as such requires that the students treat literacy as an awesome power, something that must be mastered, something that cannot be trivialized.

- One can only teach within a social, political and historical context—Nothing worth knowing exists in a vacuum—what makes what we do valuable, is that we can and do connect it to the world around us.

- A sense of fairness—Life has limits and so do the resources of our seminar. Everyone gets a chance and the work you do is what entitles you to the privilege of sharing.

- This is not about grades or abstract tests—Nothing could be further from our minds—you get credit by thinking and speaking, and writing, and reading in this seminar and the credit you get comes in the form of respect for your ideas and your creativity. Those things cannot and should not ever be turned into numbers or letters!

- Come ready to work hard—nothing truly worth having comes without hard work.

The class cannot get too large. We may have hit our limit as we approach 20-25. The students will get lost and their need to be heard will be undermined.

- A high adult-to-student ratio. We usually have at least 3 adults in the room, 4 is better as the class gets larger. Real life is a mix of ages and experiences. Our class mixes kids from all grades and adults of varying ages as well.

- Retain a sense of humor and playfulness. The work is hard but if you lose your ability to laugh—you quickly become old, boring and mean, and your feet start to smell like fish.

- Make sure the students eat well. Instill a sense of adventure in the act of eating—and be mindful of healthy food without being a fanatic.

- Team teaching—With three primary 'teachers' in the room there is a lot of intuitive skill required. What Joe and Amy and I have learned and continue to learn is how to compliment each other—too much is intrusive and confusing and too little inconsequential. It is a delicate balance and perhaps the closest thing to magic that occurs in our room.

- Flexibility—Each week I come prepared with a plan and a focus, and each week I have learned to be ready to relinquish it to deal with the important needs of the moment.

- Testing what's learned in class against the outside world—Without this component I think what we do is completely wasted. The students need to see if what we are saying and teaching has practical, applicable value in their lives. And we as teachers need to hear what works for them and what doesn't.

- Respect for the 'massa's' language, history and cultural contribution without losing perspective about the oppression embedded in it. Conversely, appreciation for the language of resistance, in our case it's called Bronxonics.

- Celebrate everyone's genius. This is not some moronic, hair-brained, utopian vision that "We are all wonderful." I have come to believe that genius is by far the most common stock in humanity. And that stupidity, if it exists at all, occurs only in the rarest of cases—chiefly in politicians. By recognizing this, and acknowledging it when observed, we build a critical positive momentum in our classroom, one that becomes self-sustaining.

- Commitment to the nuts and bolts of language mastery: Grammar, spelling, punctuation, vocabulary, structure. This is listed last because it is in many ways the most difficult to achieve and for us still remains the most elusive challenge of the project. These kids have come to us after years of what amounts to criminal educational negligence on the part of society. We work on these skills regularly but the amount of work needed to bring each student up to speed is daunting. We don't have a good solution yet but we suspect it lies somewhere in the zone between intensive individual tutoring and mentoring, mentoring of a type that may yet not even exist. Suffice it to say that many of our students feel a profound sense of shame, practice constant denial, harbor vast reservoirs of resentment, and low-self esteem as a result of these outwardly imposed deficiencies. Even for those of us who are not conspiracy theorists it is easy to see how useful and easily managed a dumbed-down population can be. But for now we continue to work hard at building self-awareness and desire in our kids so that they have the inner strength to confront and challenge their knowledge-abusers.

One of the interesting questions that inevitably arise out of an endeavor like ours is: Can it be repeated, can it be replicated in another learning environment? Is what we have done just the result of a lucky line-up of personalities and site-specific conditions? This is so often the case with projects that are driven by educators who succeed by becoming entertaining gurus. If this supposition is true, our work is profoundly less important to the rest of the world. We don't really know the answer yet. But thanks to the support of one Sallejane Seif, a well-hidden wizardess, who resides deep in the unfathomable bowels of the Department of Education, we will soon be given the chance to test our ideas in a number of other

NYC High Schools. We believe we have found something useful.

Lastly, some words of thanks to: Early Stages and its intrepid board of directors for taking a big risk on this project; to Brenda Bravo, the brave principal of University Heights who constantly runs interference for our program; to Lillian Martinez whose love and warmth keeps a school like University Heights from simply cracking apart; to the many teachers who have generously surrendered their own class time so that the students can attend our seminar; to Bronx Community college, especially Gene Adams, for patience and the gracious gift of space; to Victor who toasts and perfectly butters a bagel for me and Amy each Friday at the college cafeteria; to Maisha Tulivu Fisher, a beautiful angel, whose wings beat constantly, passing fresh-cool air over my tired eyes; to Fabienne FayLove Snowden, an apparition of hope and passion; to Amy Sultan, whose love and commitment to the students knows no bounds; to Joe Ubiles, who is without question the wisest, strongest, and most inspired teacher I've ever met; And to my young rebel writers, of course, whose courage never fails.

ROLAND LEGIARDI-LAURA
NEW YORK CITY, APRIL 2004

TO TEACH POWER WRITING

As I begin to reflect upon our work in Power Writing my first impulse is to write a manifesto, a theoretical text of methodology and praxis. The idea of authoring a manual, a schematic of structures and functions seemed compelling. This approach was accompanied by the conflicting impulse to "let the work speak"; to allow the artistry and humanity of our students to speak for itself, in both performance and print, as literature, both as evidence and artifact. The following thoughts are therefore a middle ground, both manifesto and manifestation of a body of complex ideas, experimental wisdom and praxis.

Power Writing has its origins in the very powerful idea of Paulo Freire that "education is always an act of intervention in the world." To delineate the problem of urban youth and Standard English acquisition is to restate the obvious, often without reference to mitigating factors and more often without hope of remedy. In Power Writing we value the idea of teachers as learners and learners as teachers. The knowledge that our students possess and their perceptions of the world around them are highly respected. Our concerns are rather with their linguistic interface with reality and our goal is to create a community of writers who are curious, serious, ethical and literate in the very deepest sense of these terms. We do not ignore the manifest caste and class structures of our society and we utilize the material and objective conditions of our lives as the subject of our discourse and dialogues. Writing, reading and speaking are the essential elements of Power Writing and creative writing is the medium through which the conversations of grammar, linguistics and literature are identified, examined, rehearsed and then applied in the "real world". Our students become collectors of words and therefore of ideas. It is our hope that in the acquisition of these words and ideas and in their application that the lives of these young learners will be transformed.

JOE UBILES
TEACHER

OLD SCHOOL

Eli Anchicanoy

Yasmin Arias

Carlos Brigante

Ramon De Jesus

Joel Lozada

Chantay Garcia

Alberto Luna

Charles Buddha Gomez

Adrian Martinez

Ronald Jay

Willie Navarette

Pearl Quick

Syesha Santos

LI ANCHICANOY

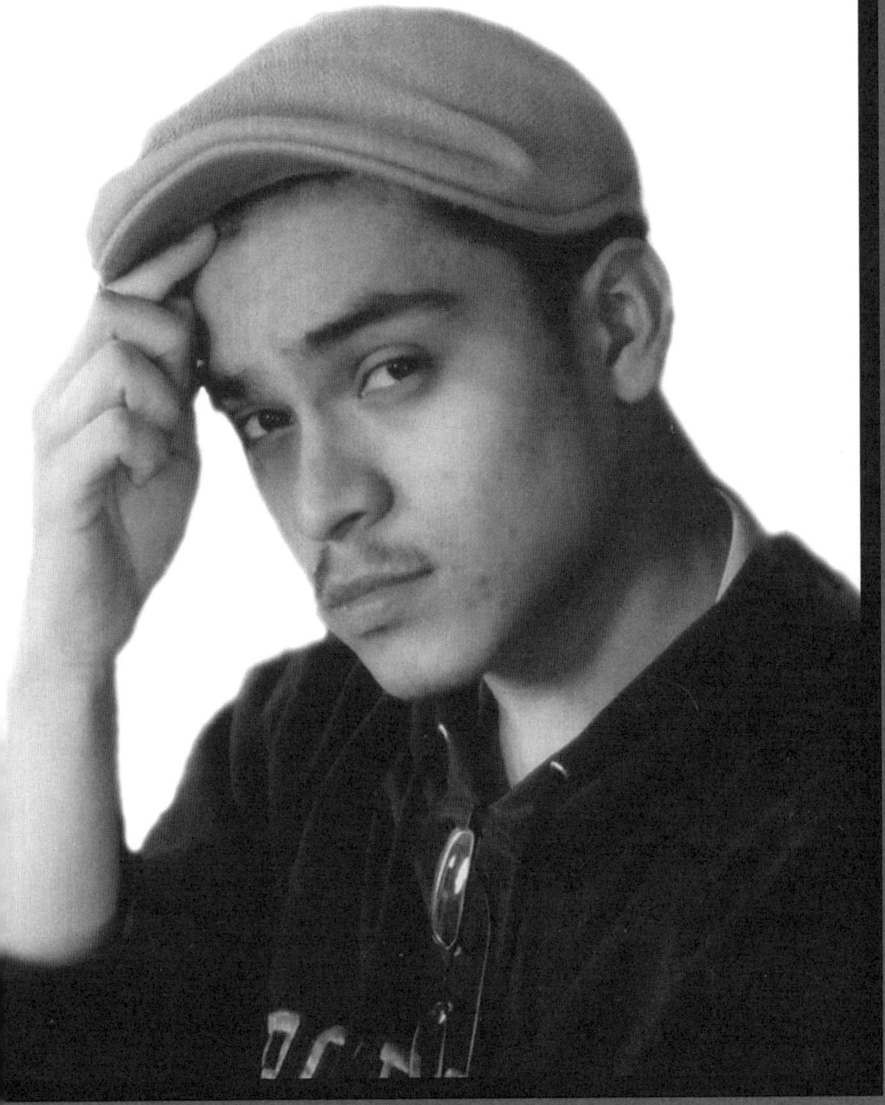

A SLAVE WHO PRESUMES TO CRITICIZE ONE'S KING–

(Inspired by a speech made by Arundhati Roy)

Ladies and Gentlemen, Allow me to introduce myself
As the Slave who presumes to criticize one's king
My identity and my ethnicity will always be a part of me
(with ease)
Rulers of the world use that as an excuse for their murders
and killing sprees
And on September 12th after 911
We become aware of a scare that will not be won.
We become aware of animosity, which will soon cease to be
Once we realize that words are a lot stronger with our
deeds.
Stop talking about the gossip and make a solution
to problems that we must act on—
That's exactly what we need.
And come September 12th, a day after that Tuesday and
that great dismay
We have to recover our health and rid the foolishness away.
We never forget exactly what was lost from us—
Commercials and the news media try to calm us,
Saying that everything will get better.
Like so-called "whatever," so to hell with that and what
attempt that might bring.
I don't want revenge, or entertainment.
I want to heal, sing and swing,
Well this is just an opinion, from a "minority" who goes
against our king.
The Media lies, changing sides
Criticize us for not wanting to follow and be minions,
But stays silent when things go wrong,
When things go wrong,
Like when their song don't go the way it was meant to.
What to do? Don't know what to do, even the third world

slave will slap us in the face, and call us fools.
Understand that they don't need to amuse us to death.
That sentence isn't recommended from the rest of us
Stand out and shout to be
The slaves, no longer slaves
Criticizing our king.

My identity and my culture
I will try to self define
By reading the writings on the walls and the halls of the
divine
Time is of the essence and a new Information Crime has
been added
The Act of Patriots in the Nation of immense information.
My children will have to face the fact that education will
be a struggle,
Now that critical thinking became regulated.
(Now I leave saying)
Our rights go balanced with our responsibilities.
Educating is awareness and our awareness we must seize!
Our time has been here and there and it won't last,
Unless we make a stand, get out of the cycle, and leave the
past.
(And focus on the present.)
For us to say our purpose is to stand out loud, walk and sing,
That for slaves to be free,
We must protest and go against our king.
(See you at a protest.)

REFLECTION BLUE–
TO MY LITTLE SIBLING WHO NEEDED THE ADVICE

Can't Rhyme and I can't write anymore
And it just might mean that it's 'cuz I haven't slept for days,
Four actually.
Lights hurt, or maybe it's just me with my sight
Because everything is like damn, 3 'o clock in the morning
And all of the light has disappeared, and yawning,
Acting like a zombie consumed by darkness,
fear of collapse.
I start looking for my pulse in my mind in order to search
for where my soul
And where my heart is at.
Little child, think about that, just for a second,
You stay up after the day is over, trying to think about what
you've done before
Now, where's the lesson in trying to be working and living
in the present if you dwell in this past? May I ask?
Stepping out of consciousness
Reality into a trance and a stare
Looking into a window with glittering essence
of the light's glare,
Staring right back.
Anybody listening to what I'm saying?
Nobody's there so nobody cares…
I begin to write in pencil before I begin to write in pen,
Now, I don't really know just what my message is until I'm
finished from
Beginning to end.
See, I really don't write the poetry, little child,
See, the reflection writes me.
It's a matter of fact,
Even in the long hours of the morning,
Near my desk and trying to write is where I'll be at.
Talking about the love and talking about the pain.

Reflection is that process that allows one to see the daytime
in the stormy rain.
To be sane using chronological sanity
With reflection, time has no meaning,
but the meaning's turning blue.
Blue, like that little window shade in my living room.
Boom! The invasion of blue seeping out of the darkness
and hitting you in the face,
Making you look into the sky and knowing you were given
this amazing grace.
How sweet is that sound? Once blind, but now I can see,
see, see.
I know the shadows are still there, but that can no longer
consume me.
Inhale and exhale, take a deep breath before I tell the tale.
Depression kills the soul so the reflection must thrust.
People hurt and end their lives thinking that in life they've
failed.
Now I ain't righteous, so try not to get that idea on me
But you're no different from me, so don't act like you're a
casualty
Be free, feel the need of love and take onto your reflection.
So word of advice, in order to make it right,
You have to reflect on your life, soul search and then decide
Where you want to go on from there.
Peace, love and god bless little sister.

ASSASSINATION ATTEMPTS IF I WERE TO BECOME PRESIDENT

My interest in my people is not the same interests as the larger extent of this country. My plans would be for economic stability for the so-called minorities. This would allow them to have a much greater participation in the economic standards of the country and the world today, by allowing minorities to build their own businesses in their own communities. If these people—who share a somewhat similar lifestyle of those people who live in third world countries—there would be new openings in the Nation's Economic businesses. Therefore, in doing this, we would have more "options" in the Capitalized style of our nation's economic standards. Is this not the Capitalistic way? If yes, then how come it hasn't happened yet? What prevents those people of low income class not to be able to support their own communities from within?

We are told, as so-called "minorities", that all we're capable of doing as a cultured people, is make sound singing and some soul dancing. I beg to differ on this primitive and prejudiced mental ideology: Yes, we can create soul and dance, but we're all capable of much more... as a cultured people! I, among many others, am living proof of such capabilities.

My overall goal is to have our people maintain the ability to determine what goes on in our own homes and communities... To advance our social and spiritual sense of standards that an oppressed people NEVER started off with oppression. If I die having done that, then, all praise is due to the creator. Any mistakes that I happen to come by are only mine.

!Pa'lante, mi gente, Pa'lante!
A fellow Latino of the human race, living in this world.

TUESDAY NIGHT'S AFTERMATH
(EPILOGUE FROM "REBELS FROM THE HEIGHTS"
EVENT)

My feelings for Tuesday night…
"Rebel Voices from the Heights"…
Oh, so I'm from the Heights now, right?
I'm from everywhere, from light to shining light and all
places from the City of New York.
This is what I was thinking about on my way
to the performance in my priest uniform.
Taking the 1 & 9 train to the L or R toward Roland's.
Writing just what kind of 3rd song I'd be able to have ready
on my way to Roland's.

Everything, like everything else, is always a blur.
I thought about my earlier performance at LaGuardia High
and comparing it to Tuesday… Just thinking about what
occurred in both events.
How did I do? How did I do?
I left Roland's thinking I couldn't be moved,
Moved by nothing unless I had music around.
I mean, I wouldn't have had anything set for the Poetry
Reflection if I wasn't moved,
Moved by the music around from the inner town…

Mainly, what I was thinking about on Tuesday night was
what I'd be able to accomplish on Tuesday that I have
already accomplished in LaGuardia.
And after the entire event was over, I was satisfied with the
work I've written.
Amazed, completely amazed with what my peers possessed.
They possessed inspiration, that's what it was for me.
I left the rugged and tired, from the rugged art loft, and yes I
was tired…
Tired, and happy as if I'd hear a faint voice say to me,

"Congratulations, now you can rest".
So, that's exactly what I do for two days…
Thinking about it now,
My memories of Tuesday is compared to
Colors of Black night, Grey clouds and "God's Thumbnail"
Sail by and away across the metro heavens outside.
Inside, staring inside orange colors,
Brown, Yellow, and white faces,
Merging as me and we,
To make music, to make music,
As one…
My memories are colors, and I was warm,
My memories are colors, and I was warm, even outside.

I'm out here now, thankful to know others—
I worry for others and care for them as they do for me.
We go about now, and took to the streets, took to the streets.
We held letters of love and grace, held clenched with our poetic sheets.
We say hello tonight and goodbye tomorrow—
See ya later now and return again some other time.
The year ain't over,
The year ain't over.
Damn, have I completely expressed what I feel for Tuesday yet?
I still have to reflect… got to reflect and write.
My work feels half-assed even though I pour out.
Let me listen to some songs,
Take a nap and work on my final poetry for today and tomorrow.
I'll be ready.
Only my peers inspire me and the music stays moving me.
Rest for today for a while,
Wake up, live and reflect for a new day…

BOHEMIAN RHAPSODY

Drops of water pass by
one's ear as if you could hear
some tales of life stories of workers passing by.
Whispers & shadows of people from the past
come back to sweetly haunt you in the morning light.
Spring in the morning
Sing in the morning
My radio cries out.
With dead souls and living souls,
of what was old is new
& what was already new
is stale & now old.
Uptown, Downtown, East Side & the West
I sit cross-legged in the center of it all
chanting the tunes & chant melodies of spiritual &
poetic prophesies.
Uptown, Downtown, East Side & the West
my sprit & mind are altogether combined after I'm aware
that I've traveled throughout my life & my home,
constantly loving and listening to new stories & old.
I strive to become an Omowale of my home & act like a
Buddha
The seasons & rain move me to become all & one,
learn from everyday fables & mysteries
studying all Bibles& Korans
of everyday love & hate
inhale, exhale towards
Downtown & Uptown
people sit cross-legged & become masters
of the Morpheus dream world
& real telling the true from the untrue,
play a little Zen on you & have you baffled & fooled.
I sit cross-legged in the middle of it all,
Nearby the rapture of pleasure.

THANK YOU SAD SHADOW

I wake up, go toward the mirror,
Questioning who I am, and why I'm here,
The typical question most people ask,
At least that's what I think.
And while I'm here in the dim sky light
A trace into my stare
I glance and remember...
You've escaped your shadows,
Marked your fists in your wife's body,
Destroyed the minds of your older sons and daughters,
Giving them a childhood of pain and insecurity;
This was even done before I was born.
To not yet have reached the world of existence
And to see this,
To not be there and to leave them
unable to shed their tears
Of hatred and pain...

As I look back I remember your shadow,
This role, an invisible role that was never there.
Surprising to know that I know what you look like,
Praying that when I stare into that mirror
Your face will never show up on mine.
You've left the very people you loved so much,
Leaving behind the trail of bruises and tears.
The torments that you gave to your wife will stay
With her until the end of her life.
She'll pass way, happy knowing that she finally
escaped from you.

I can't understand you, but I remember you.
I remember I used to hug you and
I remember hearing you tell my sisters
and me that you loved us.

You told us that we were your pride and your future.
This was something I couldn't understand...until now.
I guess you're afraid to think that I hate you.
But it's the exact opposite; I love you.
I even thank you...
Not because you ran away to the very end of existence
When I was only a child.
Not because I had a bad childhood, knowing that there
Would always be an empty place in the family photo.
Not even because you left our mother to struggle to
Carry my sisters and me on her own.
But because you are the greatest teacher and example
I have ever known.
You've taught me to give women the respect and care
That they deserve.
You've taught me never to beat my wife or run from
My family, whenever I get one...
I'm not sure what's to become of me later on,
I hope it's for good,
No, in fact I know it will be for good.
One thing I will never allow myself to become,
And that is...You.

ELI ANCHICANOY

getting heated,
It's crazy, how a perso
the advantages by, bre
ing ▓ up, (say slowly).
so, here comes the sou
the peal, that's pealin
simultaneously, give
tons of loud pealed, si
By I everyday shower
Being hereby, as I will
get vanquished, near
keeping my eye on you
franchising on amendm
send for more blotteri
You been greedy, running
and not even getting
greeted
So, why keep gatherin
All these non-senses,
repeating, or it alway
repeated,

YASMIN ARIAS

POSITIVE MIND

Look at yourself in the mirror
Ask yourself, what do I see?
A reflection of a wise man
Caught up in the triangle tangle of the system
Wanting so bad to get out of all this shit

Vision of a good life
Living right
Letting nothing hold you down
Stopping regularly
Always on the go
Reaching for my goals
That is what I know
Doing right by me
Letting no one and nothing stop me
The twisted triangles of the system
Won't have me.

REALITY

When reality finally struck me
My family, I thought to myself,
What is happening?
What is going on?
My loved ones are slowly fading away
The beautiful picture that was once there,
That rainbow picture that was once my family
Is rapidly turning into black and white.
Sadness of blackness is crossing my face
Happiness not yet there
'til everything falls into place.
My heart is feeling so cold in this time of pain.
Strength tries to overcome my body
But sadness always has the gain.
Crazy thoughts are filling my mind,
Locking me in silence, no trace behind.
Bringing myself to peace
because of all the pain he brought to me,
destruction, all that was.
Construction, never come.

Reality.

ROME, NEW YORK / THE BUS RIDE

It's 12:30AM. I wake from a short nap.
Time for me to get dressed.
Packing up food, packing up clothes,
to send it all to Rome, New York.
Going on this trip is Mommi,
my sisters Jenny, Anicia and me.
And the feeling I feel is that I really want to die.
Going to see Popi down. Why?
It's 1:30AM. We're on our way to the cab
that is waiting downstairs
taking us to Port Authority.
Now I'm on the bus and I just feel like screaming
and while I'm screaming I'm here fiending,
wanting to get high so this long, awful bus ride would stop.
I wanna drop but the fear is making me hold back my tears.
Mommi, I see her from my right and I just want to go
crazy.
I look at her and I can hear what she's thinking,
"Damn, why my baby, my husband?"
29 years of marriage, she's got six kids, me the youngest one.

3 years to life, that's what he's seeing.
And when I think about his sentence I ask,
"what is he deserving?"
"I'm scared. I don't want to see Popi like this," I'm saying
to myself.
And now we're going to visit,
One he's been planning for.
We're all in our nice clothes,
Having Popi see us in our best.
This shit is crazy. I'm so depressed.
A 4 hour visit, that's all we get.
We shouldn't be going through this shit.
"He's innocent" I say.

But he had no choice but to be a man,
Taking his wife out of this hell hole of a situation.
Now imprisoned in a jam he can't change.

I see these true lovers holding onto each other's hands
Across the table, the only allowed touch,
My parents.
They are the true meaning of love.
'Til death do them part, that is love.
Never wanting to let him go.
I can't stand to see him on this visit.
This is not his life.
He is so used to being loose,
Going and coming when he chooses.
Now the visit is over.
We had to let him go.
He had no choice but to go.
"I love you Popi", I said over and over.
"I love you, always I love you".
And his pain never showed.

YASMIN ARIAS

getting healed
It's crazy, how a perso
the advantages by; bre
ing up; (say slowly).
So here comes the sour
he peal, that's pealin
simultaneously, give
tons of loud peated, [s
by I everyday shower
being hereby, as I will
get vanquished near
keeping my eye on you
franchising on amendm
send for more blotteri
You been greedy, running
and not even getting
greeted
So, why keep gatherin
All these non-senses;
repeating or it alway
repeated.

CARLOS BRIGANTE

from my hearD changell!!!"

Title: entrapment. Dedicated to:
Writer: Carlos B. Margarita
Reason: Yow'll see. Garcia.

"One day, P.A., a real jolly girl
was so thorough that she was
also confufed. Others classi-
fied me towards her, and we were
foes. she hung out with certain
groups, those grops, I didn't trust
she was herself, busy, borique
and interested on a lot of
things. until she fell into a
slumber she hung out toomuch
she bought things that wasn't
necessary, and was against
the wrong crowd. She always
laughed, 24/7 till...
        There were rumors, confron-
tations, and beef appeared
out of nowhere. Arguments,
talks ad hate grew right there

cars roaming, buzzers ringing
and wrong advisories, back
and forth increasingly grew.
Back fires constantly, 'oh get
away from him he's no good,'
grew formal. Informality took
over, a time when I disgraced
her accidentally the circle
grew, grew, grew, until she, I
believe suicided herself from
confusion. she was a flesh
of my flesh, blood of my blood
but she stepped into a mud
pull where no one could get
off from. Today, I pray....''

Title: the worse thing that
ever happened to me.
Writer: Carlos B.
Reason: Resolution.

''One morning woke up, went
to the store, bought poor

snacks, and I smelled something bound to happen. Relaxing,
conversating, and doors knocked
(boom, boom, boom, it's the police)
My two sisters, and I, ran into
our room, they sat down I gten
mad. I said "F**** that I'm
not going down without a fight"
they bombarded the door
threw my mother to the ground,
and hearing whispers of cries
roaming. Foot steps running,
running, then came to the room
where we were. It was a fight.
A fight of strength against
strength, I wasn't strong e-
nough they won, I flew back
I demanded me to sit I yelled
(No, they shoved me down with
one hand, left arm, flewdown
to the sofa real hard.
They stopped, think it
felt like my life was over.

RAMON DE JESUS

AND THEY COLOR THEM BLUE

The words flow through my veins
And vowels are my reds and whites
I would just like to say Motherfuck You!
Now that I got that off my chest
Let's talk about the rest.
I write about big sisters
And I love me some breasts
I write about the world
I write about the earth
And I hate it when women
Talk about a man's length and girth
I write about peace
I write about war
I write about Lewinsky
Sucking dick on all fours
I write about Bush
I write about Dick C.
I write about choking on pretzels
I write about terror
I write about Bin laden
I write about 9/11
I write about a million virgins
Waiting for them in heaven
I write about books
I write about wigs spit so hard
Turn the tree on your limbs
Into leaves and twigs
I write 'cause I can,
I write 'cause I will
And like Jay Z said
"Fuck 50 Cent
I'm about dollar bills."

THE SPEEDING TICKET

So I got a…

Bitch sucking my stiffy while I do one hundred and 50…
Eyeing the wet twat, then I hear sirens of cops coming to
get me…

Pulled over, cop said, "Ya should be stopping at the red"…
Then I speed off, tires kicked and lodged a rock in his fore-
head!!!
Fuck! You'd think after murderin' a police in a freak accident…
Hoe's mouth'll cease slurpin' and release what the freak has
in it…
I'm thinking of my court case and jurors lobbying a
sentence…
THUMP!!! Shit, I just ran over the body of Jimi
Hendrix!!!…
15 cops chasin'…I tell the panicking chick to just chill…
as I try to wipe Hendrix brain matter off my windshield…
Flying on the interstate, wondering how my mind just went
away…
"I need a plan", then bitch's hand flashes a 9 in up in my
face!!!
She's like "Run ya money sonny nuttin' funny, don't even
try it!
I'm like "Wasn't ya tonguin', sucking my stuff with semen
smiling?…
And I got the cops blastin' shots, then my ass in a slick
move…
Ducks the slugs & smashed the broad in the passenger win-
dow!!!
Damn! Now that body tally's 3 with some army after me…
Then 2 cops go to both sides of my car and sandwich me…
Ramming me right and left in pain, I think the next
facade…

Is dead to these jakes, and I hijack the adjacent Escalade...
I press the brakes, release the car from it's jammed place-
ment...
Grab the bitch's 9 milli & shoot the cops gas tanks in!!!
Evading explosion my car flops, stutters with thud sounds...
Turn to the Escalade, 9 raised like, "Stop the Fuckin' Truck
Now!!!"
But the driver ignored, Okay...this hoe wants a casket!
So I shot the driver, leaving heat in that Cold Hearted
Bastard...
I'm cashing through b-cades...then I gasp when I see a...
50 foot gap in the freeway, but I punch the gas to just
'Speed' fate!!!

Then I...wake up! Swerving with this chick up in the
Bentley...
Bitch sucking my stiffy while I do one hundred and 50.

MICROPHONE

yo the microphone i'm gripping it and start ripping shit
flowing limitless when sparking cigarettes and drinking
guinessess
it's the most infinite intricate intellect in this bitch
my written is like a grave because niggas is digging it
when it comes down to clitoris
some niggas put their lips in it
some niggas put their fists in it but i just put my dick in it
i hate cats talking 'bout the slum but never been in it
i hate cats talking 'bout owning a gun but never triggered it
i'm pitiless, killing lyricists in front of witnessess
i'm 'bout to lyrically take your life so nigga "gimmie it"
this rhyme is so hard i sprained my ankle from kicking it
flipping the illest script even syphilis is sick of this
i'm articulate, i'm only guilty of being innocent
i'm giving you this style for free just because i'm generous
my image is rigorous that's why niggas try to mimic it
if i compete i'll be awarded whatever the winner gets
it's ridiculous how you're the total opposite of literate
i suggest Joe take away your poetry writing privileges.

MY BROTHER

The car. The car hit so hard it was in front of the horn. Teeth were shattered, Brown frame mangled, as he dragged himself out of the car. My brother, whom I love to death, has just been in a car accident. And I am afraid to lose him. In the hospital crying for mom, but his screams are muffled. His mouth held together by twisting feet of metal wires, and his jaw held in place by a metal monster. Slurred speech, drinking soup, no solid foods. He was always angry after it, and took it out on me. But I loved him and took it in stride. Day after day tending to his needs, bringing him his soup, and his bucket to spit in. When he was back on his feet, he was back in the streets. I would call and get no answer, he was gone once again. The pain, the screams, the mental beating, all gone. In its place remains a void, where I only see his face on drunken nights. If I get up early enough I can catch him coming back from a night out with his friends. Arms wrapped around his knees, but the legs keep moving and the little boy gets pushed to the side where he wonders where his brother has disappeared to. Mother screams and throws platanos, while I'm caught in the crosshairs of the verbal warfare. Kids on the way, but he continues his way. Until it happens again. Once again I am his proud little servant. Bucket in one hand soup in the other. But I know once he's better, the arms will not hug back.

RAMON DE JESUS

CHANTAY GARCIA

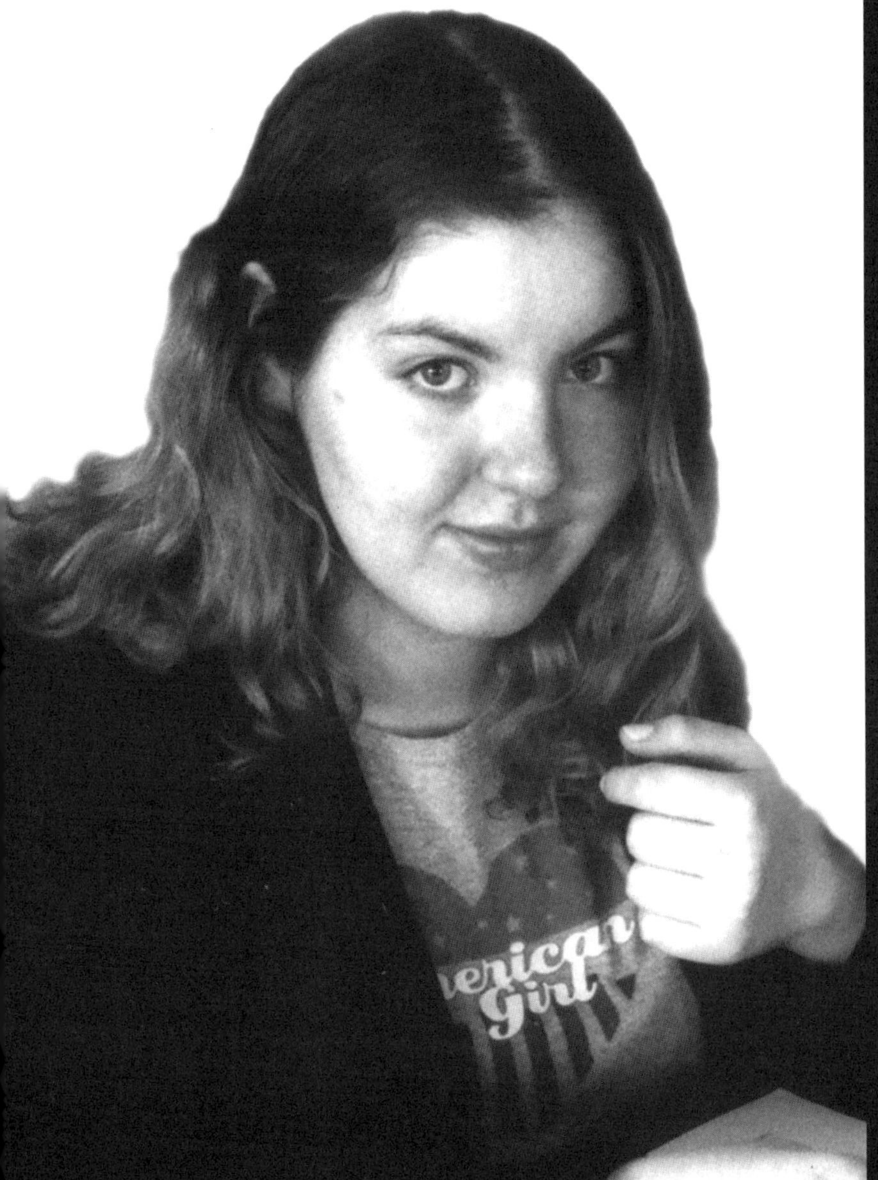

I WANT TO WRITE ABOUT...LUST

Sex
Love,
Greed
Vengeance
Music
The Beatles
Passion
Sensuality
Death
Creation
Life
Conception
Intelligence
Racism
War
Violence
Peace
Harmony
Sexuality
Vindication
Religion
The President
Nirvana
Intentions
Soul-Mates
Healing
Madness
Anger
Happiness
Sadness
Hatred
Heartache
Friendship
Enemies
Kurt Cobain

John Lennon
Blood Brothers
Johnny Cash
Politics
A cure
Stupidity
Elvis
Punk Rock
Hard Rock
Rock-and-roll
Vanity
Insanity
Exile
Internment
Camps
Angels
Devils
Inner-Demons
Skeletons
Men
Women
Atheists
Kings
Queens
Periods
Affirmatives
2003
Holidays
Loneliness
Psychos
Homosexuals
God
Jesus
The Bible
New York City

Ireland
Patriot Act
Animal Cruelty
Cruel and usual
punishment
Children
Siblings
Drowning
The stars
Purity
Innocence
America
The American
Family
The American
Dream
The loss of
Innocence
Stardom
Teenage Mothers
Drugs
Liquor
Food
Drunks
Drug addicts
Role Models
Ex-Boyfriends
My Knife of
Romance
Crossroads
Submission
Masochism
Domination
Sadism
Hypocrites

Terrorists
Colorado
Welfare
Pink Slips
Materialism
Abandonment
Cheating
Humility
Aggressiveness
Meekness
Inspiration
Riots
Muses
Guardians
Slaves
Viruses
Dick Cheney
Lake Of Fire
Unions
Marriage
Obeying
Abuse
Poisoning Minds
Anarchy
Desire
Zen
Japan
Feudalism
Democracy
Liberalism
Totalitarian
Picasso
Beethoven
Frank Sinatra
The Clash
Punk Rockers
Goths
Preps
Poseurs
Sellouts

Criminals
Pink Floyd
HIV
AIDS
STD's
Addictions
Valium
Prozac
Exuberance
Youth
Ageism
Motivation
Holiness
Wholeness
Girl Power
Sluts
Whores
Escorts
Strippers
Money
Economics
Wall Street
Manhattan
The Village
Pennsylvania
Hicks
Hickeys
Affection
Lack of
Affection
Juveniles
Movie Stars
Rock Stars
Jimi Hendrix
The Doors
Bills
Imagination

…I just want to
write.

CLUTCHING THE SIDES

Clutching the sides,
Bruised and rain soaked.
The sea beyond thrashing and churning.
and chains still bind me,
For years this has been my fallback.
My wall is my safe place,
where I don't receive the pain.
Now I want to let it go,
their names carved in the stones.
Each tear put these stones into place.
The white dress I wear is ripped and stained,
from trying to fight my chains.
It's fear that ties me still.
Fear of the unknown
Fear of vulnerability
Fear of the pain that comes from you.
Is it really time to set myself free?
I find the key and unlock my cuffs,
I begin to stand and fall.
The sharp stones that litter the earthen floor
of my cell cut into my pale flesh.
The stinging pain, brings no tears to my eyes.
I stand and stumble to the gates,
my blood dripping around me
and on my white dress.
I unlock the gate, hands shaking.
I walk through into the daylight.
I'm free.
But why does it feel like I'm drowning?

EACH TOUCH IS DIFFERENT

Each touch is different, like snowflakes,
made of broken glass and razorblades.
Your kisses are a flash fire of pain.
Why can't you see me?
WHY!?
I don't want to be your plaything anymore, please?
Turn down the stage lights.
My make-up is running down my face like an ocean.
Chain me to your coffee table,
wearing only a scowl and Prada pumps.
I'm still chained to you from miles away.
That's right, get close,
so I can see what your false mask looks like.
I wonder how I can make you asphyxiate yourself
on your own tongue.
I feel my scream rise up, but stop at my eyes.
It swims in my mind,
choking every thought.
There are no more tears,
just an empty hollow space of emotions.
I misplaced love, especially my love for you.
So enjoy your paradise. . . . . .

NOISE POLLUTION

It's streets are filthy with garbage and dog poop.
It's full of wannabe thugs,
that hang out in from front of the library
but they can't read.
Most of the children are disrespectful,
as are their 16 year old mothers.
Drug deals are done out in the open instead of in private.
More drug deals being done in front the McDonalds.
Graffiti on the church,
and all over this long forgotten gem.

(3/6/03)

Tears streaming down little girls faces.
Angry words thrown left and right.
The knife cutting the right way
Is suicide their right way
Is there really a place
where all the lost souls go?
Bright eyes and bright smiles
How well they mask the pain.
I see through straight to the core.
It's as if they bleed.
 I pray for their salvation.
My little seraphim
But I can't protect them anymore.
how I wish I could teach them .
But there's no more I can share.
So I weep when they die
and the cycle continues.

CHANTAY GARCIA

CHARLES BUDDHA GOMEZ

CHARLES "ANTI-BUDDHA" GOMEZ
20 YRS. OLD
WASHINGTON HEIGHTS, NEW YORK

I often find solace in the writing of poetry. It expresses my angst against the loss of my childish flights of fancy and being grounded by logic or perhaps it's just my escape from mathematics. You see, poetry is the voice which haunts me and brings me to my knees to fry out in that sullen tone. Some ask "what is the purpose of my poetry? Humor, anger, ignorant bliss?" well…no. simply put it's my attempt to leash the mischievous monster that I know resides in all living things. And in a small way take difficult and perplexing events and emotions and try in some way to make sense of it. So I hope that the dozens of readers around the world enjoy my ramblings.

P.S. Thank you to Joe, Amy, Roland, and Early Stages, all of which made my voice available to the world. Without you guys my poems would only have the potential to take up memory on my computer. Thank you. I'll never forget this.

I WONDER

I found myself half asleep
Against a young birch tree
The cool grass tickling my feet
My eyes closed to take in the warm breeze
And the touch of the setting sun.
Then I heard it,
A faint breath,
I heard her smile before her voice
I felt her cut through the air so
Gracefully and divinely
I smelled the flowers she had been
Picking that afternoon
My eyes just in time fell open to
See her walk into the horizon
As if straight into the sun
And as I smiled it was dark
So what now?
How am I supposed to feel?
Your memory is fading
And pain is all there is that reminds me of you.

I HELP

There was a cat stuck up in a tree
So I cut down the tree
And the cat died.

Then there was a boy trapped in a well,
So I filled it to make him rise
But he didn't survive.

And then there was a man stuck
under the wheel of a car,
So naturally I helped by starting the car
and driving off,
And now he is gone.

I went to lunch and a man was choking,
So I punched him in the stomach.
I cracked a rib in him that punctured his lung.

I mean, I try to help
But nothing seems to go right for me today at all.
Now I'm off to work at the hospital.

ROAMING

Whilst staggering through the road
I found myself a nucleus to a desert
Slowly sinking into it
My form stood indifferent with my soul
My faith fighting to revert
My heart wanting to submit
Then the twilight arrived like art
I appeared as a bust on an earthen shelf
Chiaroscuro leaning on the darkness
What other dungeon is as dark as ones own heart?
What jail so impenetrable as ones own self doubt?
Hawthorne was correct in his words expressed
Now in the darkness a voice of light
A simple offer of a second chance
A chance my character along the road did not merit.
I contemplated if it was right
Then began to slowly move my hands
Held my chest and acted like I did not hear it.

UNFORTUNATE BOY

Who will watch over this boy
as he sleeps in the dark wood?
Who will protect this boy
in the valley of shadows?
Who will guide this boy through
the labyrinth of moving walls?
Who will carry this boy
when he cannot bear
the hot sands of time?
Who will cry for this boy
when he cannot cry anymore?
Who will do these things
for this unfortunate boy,
this boy I used to be?
For this boy that we all
once were at some point?
I will…I always have, you know.

WHAT WAS THE QUESTION?
NOVEMBER 8, 2003

I write to fuck up the English
language,
to go to Russia and talk me some
Spanglish,
to debate world leaders and
make them look average.
I write to make the sane line
blur,
to remind us of who we once
were,
to one day be cloaked in fur.

I write to make it rain every
day,
to make you do as I say,
to cheat, to pillage, to zone out and
slay…

For all those that don't know who I am,
for the child, for the man,
I write because I can.

CHARLES GOMEZ

getting healed,
It's crazy, how a perso
the advantages by, bre
ing up? (say slowly).
So, here comes the sou
the peal, that's pealin
Simultaneously, give
tons of loud pealed, s
By # everyday shower
Being hereby, as # will
get vanquished, near
Keeping my eye on you
franchising on amendm
send for more blotter
You been greedy, running
and not even getting
greeted
So, why keep gatherin
All these non-senses,
repeating, or it alway
repeated,

RONALD JAY

AMY'S CHALLENGE ANSWERED

Many achievements blinded me when I was young
I felt wanderless/destruct/lost
So I had those negative images that came over me/
Leaving my thoughts/Going insane
So I just see death
I walk the train seeing others in their caskets
& I just sit there feeling like I was 10
& there my grandmother exists/
I learn she was a fiend
And then my father appear/handing me a gun
What was I to do on someone I hate
Disappear? Never was I to see my father again/
So I found that I don't fit in the crowds
So you a good student boy
Achieving many things/flip the script
U can't write poetry boy/ u ain't no poet/
They get in my head/distinctly destructive
Mentally injecting me/crushing my thoughts
They planted a disease in me
that I'm a nigga
Oh teacher, please, I'm not a nigga
I just want to live happily
But you say that 2/ don't u hide my images
Please, I just want to express myself
And now I feel naked where my mother
Put clothes on me/
Hi mommy, please comfort me
Tell me to stop crying
Why is these images haunting and blunting me/
So my thoughts are a stream like rivers
Back in the negative world
I have held a gun
So he like guns/ but I think no one knows
Flo 2 wanted to die/

No one was there to talk to me but my grandmother
And then God took her away/
Why in the fuck will he do that
So I walk in the path of streams
My thoughts sliding upon other thoughts
That just seem lost
Is this my trap?
Is it just that I want people to hear me
Or is it that I want them to understand
That I was a child when he split in front of me
The negative capture me
No one heard me in love/ hurt or ever dead
Yes, my life is dead
So what has resurrect is the sorrow
That I borrow from the world
Words that brand the blackest sun marks
Onto my skin.

I SPIT /EARTH DAY

I spit
I spit and I spit
See thru the man's eye
He starts to see himself thru the mirror waters that drown
his soul
See the rain touches my mud skin/ like tears that are gin,
I just hold on to Mary
I build Egyptian pyramids that only build my soul/
It's a nigga, my black friends
Medusa's eye catches me and turns my rock stone eyes
That make my body solid
I fall in love with the river
Make love to the river
Only so that I drown with the river
The air starts to pollute my body
Like the cops start to shoot my soul
Those raindrops erase the cotton off my skin
The mud buries me in the quicksand
Where I feel handicapped and
Can't feel my hands, lost through the tear of
My skin like a Perdue
My thoughts are like a petunia
My heart like a dandelion
Come find my eyes as the sun cracks on the dirt soil
Then watch African couples give birth to beautiful
African women
I start to watch villages, as well as cities and countries,
burn like the Negroes Lightning that is trapped in the
bottle that they are afraid to let go of
See through those men's eyes

They start evaluating their self though the swamp
That buries their dicks
The earth shoots me
Watch the disease that's trapped in my soul
Just like the lightning that's trapped in my eyes
I just flush the dirt off my skin.
I'm scared of the earth

THE GUN

My tears are my gun that burns when it reaches
other eyes
The world is my gun that burns when it reaches our
eyes like the sun
I'm dying inside of my mother/ I die
The world seems different
Everyone in a different mood/ see the vibe from my
indifferent body/
my indifferent eyes are beside me
it held the black importance
I'm just the image
We all niggas
We all hold guns running from the white man
Gun is my mind
Is a jail
Thoughts are golden bars that surround me
It's hell when the world isn't well/
I'm shackled in the prison jail
I'm a hypocrite/
In guns I trust my bloodshot eyes
And from the revolver
The purple world cries in my eyes
We all cried
My eyes are the burner

RONALD JAY

JOEL LOZADA

BREATH OF THE UNBOUND DESTINY

The changing tides
Finally made up my mind
I raise my hand from
far beneath the shifting sand
and embrace the winds of change

Suddenly everything is up to me.
Pages turn flashing full of memories.
I can see it all too clear,
The time has come to face my fears.
And there's a fire burning
 In my heart to shine when all is torn apart

I will make it through
Any devil's storm, safe and warm
My shield is strong
I'll take my chances here and now.

Bring on the fight
I'll find a way to win some love.
For tomorrow's no regrets
I'll risk it all
For this brand new day.

KIKYO
MY LOVE

I will always remember you
You are of water, earth and grass
Your soft, sweet scent
And how smelling your hair
Tickled my face like flower petals
The way your eyes made the stars jealous with their light
How your jet black hair reflected all the brilliance
Of the world's night sky
How your skin would glow like the moon
And how when I was a boy I thought you were made
of snow

Kikyo
I'm wondering if your delicate sandaled feet
still tread soil with graceful strokes
or are you skipping clouds and
watching the world over the shoulder of your wings
gliding through heaven like the most beautiful living
ornament
that has ever graced the sky

Kikyo
Where are you?
Are those two dark, deep shining lakes
Still looking at me from afar?
Will your heartbeat ever find its way to me
And with every beat give rhythm to my life?

Kikyo
Come back to me
Fulfill me, girl made of diamond dust
And breath of fire, other half of my soul.

LILITH

Mother of the flightless angels
Are the women of the world.
Gentle, caring, strong and passionate
Are the words that don't begin to describe them
Because they define those words.
Women have always been the guardians,
The treasurers of peace for our
Past, present and future.
They have been the mightiest warriors
In cooling men's strife.
They have been all too kind with
Pathetic, self-conscious men.
She had been all too patient with Adam
And should be reasonably spiteful
Of the subservient Eve.
Women have been the true faces
Of forgiveness and generosity
Throughout the history of this human experiment.
However women are not lies,
Women are Lilim
And the men of the world are their children,
The hephilim of the Dark Prince.
Women are patient, inherently wise rebels
Who are as beautiful as the most
Brilliant jewels of the Earth.
Ironically, the Earth is Mother,
The Earth is Lilith,
The Earth is beautiful.

STAR SUMMONING

Wishing for a dream that seems far off,
Hoping it will come today.
Into the starlit height
Foolish dreamers turn their gaze.
Wishing on a shooting star,
But what if the star is not to come?
Will their dreams fade to nothing?
When the horizon darkens
How do we all believe there is hope?
Is an angel watching closely over me?
Can there be a guiding light I've yet to see?

I know my heart should guide me, but
There's a hole within my soul.
What will fill this emptiness inside of me?
Am I to be satisfied without knowing?
I wish then for a chance to see,
How all I need is my star to come.

JOEL LOZADA

getting healed,
It's crazy, how a perso
the advantages by; bre
ing ♦ up; (say slowly).
So, here comes the sour
the peal, that's pealing,
simultaneously, give
tons of loud pealed, br
By I everyday shower
Being hereby, as I will
get vanquished near
keeping my eye on you
franchising on amendm
send for more blotteri
You been greedy, running
and not even getting
greeted
So, why keep gatherin
All these non-senses;
repeating, or it alway
repeated,

ALBERTO LUNA

MY NAME IS ALBERTO LUNA.

I was born and have spent the majority of my life in the United States. I currently reside in the Bronx, and attend high school at University Heights. My poems usually dwell on the general topic of love, but when another topic of great relevance arises, I write on them as well. This is a topic of great relevance. Up to my current age of of 17, I have been rather indifferent to the ordeals of politics. However, I have not been ignorant to the immediate correlation between it and war, and the hazards war has on people. I simply wish poems such as mine open people's eyes, and possibly help them to avert redundant losses of life.

CLOCKING IN

Being a man is being a provider.
Wake up man, it is time to go to work.
Get up, get dressed.
Put on that tidy clean uniform
that thieves you of your uniqueness and personality.
Do not forget that name tag.
You want people to be able to differentiate you from the
other ants.
Get on that crowded bus that has not even saved some
space for wind.
Almost start a fight with the guy who is trying to get to
the back of
the bus by knocking everyone else over.
Get to your job.
Clocking in.
Walk by your fellow workers who wave whenever you're
in sight,
then talk and mock you behind your back.
Walk by your boss and shake his hand.
He'll congratulate you on a job well done,
telling you that you're his best employee.
Then he'll dock hours from your check
because they accumulated to more than he expected.
Of course you are his best employee; you are working
for free.
Break your back and sweat, picking up boxes as heavy
as you are.
Put up with the wrath of frenzied customers
who yell at you because your company doesn't have their
favorite brand,
and do nothing about it because you want to keep your
job.
Spend the whole day selling product you'll never see a
dime for,

and there's no time for your break,
but it will get taken out of your check anyway.
After picking up the mess made by savage buyers,
you ask if you could leave.
After a couple of extra assignments and redundant
runarounds,
he'll let you go.
Finally.
Started at 9AM, left at 11PM. Not bad. Clocking out.
Wait a half an hour or so for the bus that rarely passes at
that time of night.
Get off and drag yourself home. Fumble through your
keys,
open the door. Enter and fall flat on your face.
Whatever. At least it puts food on the table. Part of being
a man I guess.
It's modern day slavery with verbal whippings and a lousy
check.
But you're a man, and that's life.
Oh shit wake up man, it is 7am. Get dressed,
get back on the stupid bus, get to work.
Clocking in…

IF

If my life were to cease
and my soul flee from my corpse
may God permit me to return
as a strand of your hair
so I could always be there,
directly connected to your wonderful mind.
I'd wish to return as your saliva so every time
you moisten your lips I could taste them.
I'd return as the tears in your eyes so
that when you weep I could sacrifice
drops of myself and within each drop I'd store
as much of your pain as I could and rid you of it.
My added incentive would be my caress
of your cheek on the way down your face.
I'd return as a sound and be privileged as you listened.
I'd return as the sunrise
so I would be the first to greet you each morning
and be blessed to be the first thing your beautiful eyes see.
I'd return as water so that I would be able to tease you
when it rains,
quench you when you thirst, feel you when you bathe.
If my life were to cease
and my soul flee from my corpse
I'd prefer it would be in your arms
so I could return to love you once again.

MY PRIVILEGE, MY DOWNFALL

Seeing the man that this image portrays,
his eyes diverted from whatever nature it is that calls his
name,
and his expression is blank, like the white that surrounds
his pupils.

What do you see?

Do you see a man who looks to his side and admires what
the world is today?
Or do you see a man who is too ashamed to look at what
lays before him?
There is nothing vindictive about his stare
yet there is nothing promising about his absent smile.

Who is he?

Is he the hero of every damsel's dream?
Or is he the flower chewed by a running lawnmower?
Is he the genius destined to succeed?
Or is he the fool who expects and foresees
his own failure?

His face gives away nothing. No emotions, only a percep-
tion of indifference,
like the stray bullet from the gun of a drunk.
Who could tell if his face has been caressed more by a
kiss of a lover,
or a tear of a broken heart?

The picture is as colorless as his gesture.

But who could tell if his life has an excess of color, or is
in desperate need of it?

A picture tells a thousand words but are these words
understood?
Or just nonsensical drivel dispersed like the stars
of the night?
Can you see if this being is happy,
or empty like a politician's promise?

Who is he?

I, for one, can say who he is, for I have stared into his eyes
for many years when I look into the mirror.
However, there are times when I cannot answer these
questions myself.
For this, I neither loathe him nor love him.
With me or without me, he is still alone.
And me being him is both
my privilege and my downfall.

THE BEEHIVE

A flower with thorns…
A rose of beauteous nature, and divine scent
Conversely, avert coming in contact
For sharp needles are there to penetrate your skin.
These sharp needles will pierce your heart.
A breath-taking goddess, with eyes that entrance you in
seconds
And a face so fair it shines with a light that can dry tears.
However she lies in the core of a field of scattered,
broken glass.
Is it worth the risk?
It's like fearing to inhale the marvelous aroma of a meadow
to not intake a deadly disease.
Like walking blindfolded alongside the edge of a cliff,
hazard, peril…
A hive of honey, the most delicious honey a human can
taste
The hive may beckon you, but alas…you may be stung
by its bees.
Now tell me, is it worth the risk?
Can you choose between a doubt and a wound?
A wound can pierce your skin, your heart and your soul.
It can scar you and cause you agony that may make you
tremble,
weep and die inside.
But a doubt can annoy you. It can persist and remain
with you forever.
Tell me now…is it worth the risk?

TITANS INDIFFERENT TOWARD OTHERS

Pillage, burn…the fire of his eyes scalded all those close enough to breathe the same air as he. His words…knives that pierce through the hearts that have been opened up to accept him in. Confuse those words with pillows as they seep out of his mouth like poison gas out of air vents. His kisses tease and excite the opposite sex enough to make a half oval appear beneath her nose and between her lips. Is it only I who sees the snake tongue that crawls out of his wretched mouth? Whispers cruel nothings in her ear. Deafen her to what she thinks is a violin and really is the screeching sound of nails on a blackboard. What game is this you play? Progressing through the levels of her trust, defeating the bosses using cheat codes. Finally you triumph, defeating the last master…her heart. What now? You won, only to crush the prized heart in your hands and watch as her blood spills on the floor. Hear me now Goliath. Call me David. My shield is composed of love, mine and hers. A weapon is what I don't need. You are a Titan, but not a man. I will slay you by mending what you destroyed and leave you at the mercy of envy and contrition.

ALBERTO LUNA

getting healed
It's crazy, how a pers[on]
the advantages by; "bre[ak]
ing up" (say slowly).
So, here comes the sou[nd]
the peal, that's pealing
Simultaneously, give
tons of loud pealed, 5
By 7 everyday shower
Being hereby, as I will
get vanquished near
keeping my eye on you
franchising on amendm[ent]
send for more blotter
You been greedy, running
and not even getting
greeted
So, why keep gatherin[g]
All these non-senses,
repeating, or it alway[s]
repeated

ADRIAN MARTINEZ

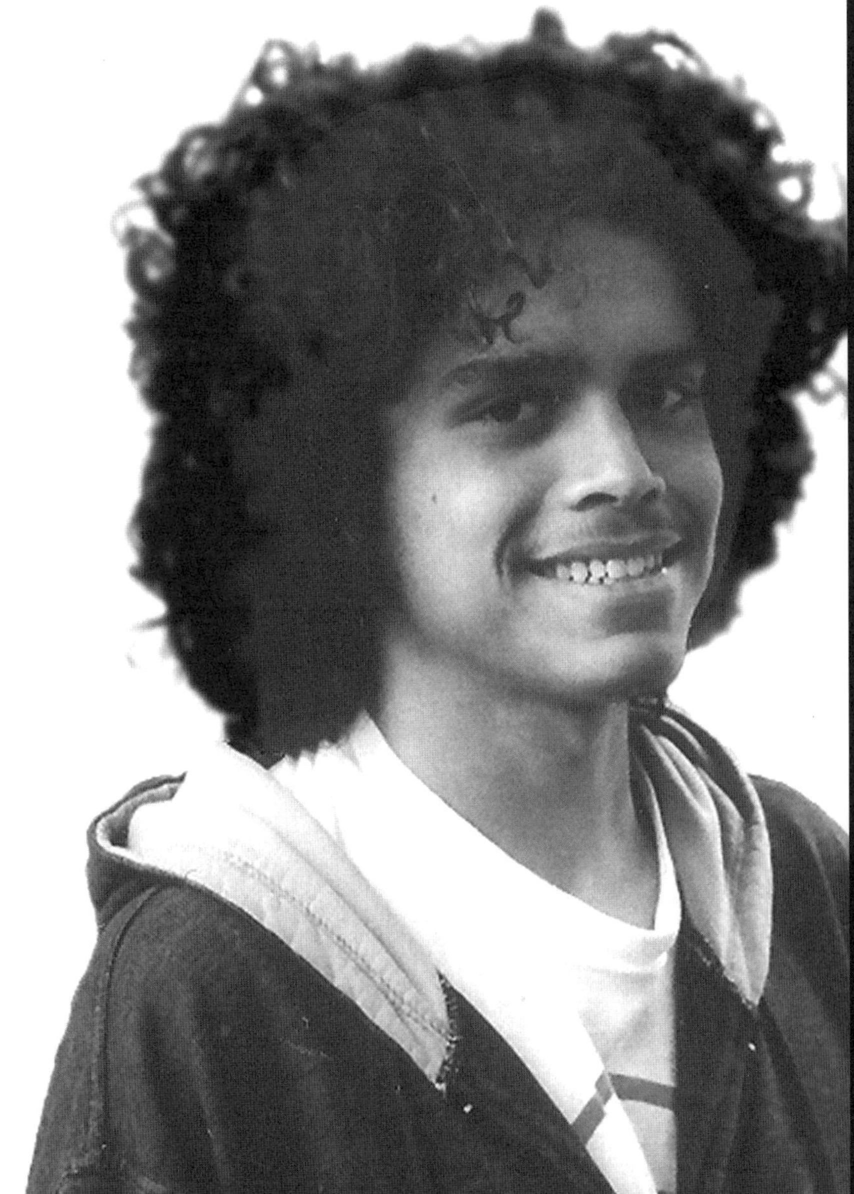

AN INSULT FOR THE DAMNED

I picked up the pen today as if it mattered
I yearn for meaning.
Try to discover it within these vacant words. Nothing
They won't speak anymore than they have been spoken
for,
so I weep, to sit in solitude, hoping for solidarity
who'll never take my hand.
And so I will secrete my woe into wine and
drink its bitterness
'till I choke on self-disgust.
Please pity me so I can join the casualty list of your
detachment,
Like a churchgoing sinner, apologizing for the death of
my sister.
Save your sorrow if you have not loved her, held her
and slice your tongue for preaching salvation.
Then can you let the blood flow crimson red to the
blackest sludge
and watch it wash over the world until it rots.
Now, where is the horse you rode in on,
Knocked from its bones with its soul split?
Where is the stallion that sang melody and companionship?
I believe he fell to the heavens, upon his knees,
into clouds of powder and sand.
I am sorry for your loss, truly, and hope that one day,
within my vacant words, you too can understand.

GRAND

She has withered hands, hands like branches
Bent and crooked like a lie
All too often she lies to herself, denies herself
And she's lonely
Fallen man, fallen boy, they were both just boys
But only one had an excuse for being a boy, not for dying
And the other died with an excuse for dying
Reluctant tears peek bitter sweet at the photos face down
in the frame
It's sad really, it makes me sad
I've watched her waste from afar
I have done nothing; I feel it is such a waste
What kind of person am I?
A boy, just like a man, as a boy, as a son?
Crooked lies, crooked spine
A crippled hip, not a crippled mind. I wouldn't know
I've never tried, have not the time
All excuses fly, I'll go. I lie.
And alone she lies in bed at home
Confined to a home where Gladys and Margie visit
More than mommy and daddy
Like father, like son, like prison, like a home
Outside becomes a holiday, occasions fulfill a dream
Another photo falls face down in the frame
We are all just children in a playground
Leaving her on an empty swing
At the bottom of a rung-less ladder
There is no escape for aging, only embracing
And we have lost our arms
Have kissed them all goodnight
What a curse to outlast them till their end!
What a shame to see them come and gone, loved and lost

Crying out dust that crusts the eye blind
The heart sags
It tremors like the waves from a marble dropped
in a vat of blood
Maybe a cannonball
Neglecting the end, owning the bliss of dying
Not now, not like this
The painful abyss of a toxic mind
So my children die, they become hours
Hours are minutes just in minutes
In a minute, okay!? Full of hours
So slow for Grand. It's so loud
Familiar faces turn embossed silhouettes rushing away
Speeding far until desertion

So it flies

My crooked lies
Her crippled hip now a crippled mind
I wouldn't know
I've never tried, I have all the time
So much time. I'll go. I'll cry
And alone she lies in bed at home
With this occasion fulfilling a dream
And another photo fallen, face down in the frame.

HER RISING TWILIGHT

face to face
    Our hands embrace at our sides
chin to shoulder, face to chest
    The echoes of our drums beat in harmonic a cappella
so gently touching as if hovering
naked above the dew dropped grass
without the morning's cold but its cool
Yet the heat of its electricity makes every pore-covered
inch of my being secrete the
Shivering sweat of her majesty
    my supreme ruler
Governing none but myself to her will

    And she inspires sensations that no earthly sense
    or measure can record or remember
    until her muse inspires once more

palm to palm
    Lips locked in admiration of exchanging tastes
and her hair flows like a chaotic silhouette that eclipses
the light of the sun like the moon
etching an evolving shadow that bores away at the floor,
yet harms me not
Such a being could not wield pain
And she descends to grace my person with her phantas-
mal elegance
Inspiring unearthly sensation that my body will forget but
my mind remember
Enlightening my flesh, bursting with joy that language
could never express
Like a lightning of breeze
A thunder of delight trembling in syncopated rhythm

We hold our breaths, then we breathe
She envelops and opens a path to my breast,
Then she leaves

MY HOOD

Check out my hood. It covers my head. Pressing my hair

My hood was green for a time then it changed and changed

When I got it, it was free and fresh

Worth all the money in the world

Then it was bleached, then soiled, then worthless

It would drop and draw, clear and fissure

Letting the rain in to drip in on my head

Bleeding greens, bleach, the black and the blues

The hues of the things living in my hood

I love them all though they itch and pinch, but I dig

And out come the colors, the dirt, the grime

Tossed in a blender, speed washed to a bloody slime

Snarling with threads, fleeing out towards the night

Weaving the sky. Leaving me, loving me

Gazing under its twilight amazed by its life

Welcome to my hood

ADRIAN MARTINEZ

WILLIE NAVARETTE

CREATION

Nature made major play doh that we shape
As the earth's second hand controller.
The assistant coached provoked.
Diverse purpose emerged
From first man and woman,
Adam and Eve or the galaxy's revolution.
Eventual future pollution improving circuits misery.
Stripped from 100% freedom
the government will never be capable of.
Jail systems that increase incarceration
claiming discipline really slip on the job.
Baby Moms without fathers won't ever find a cure
to save the children,
unless we bring
immediate family to complete up-bringing.
Twisted combinations in this world's tying of the laces.

OUT OF SPITE

Out of Spite I spike
my punch lines to divide strands of sanity.
It won't be much longer until I am claimed insane
And locked up in a loony bin with Bin Laden
Or Saddam Hussein
Who's sane these days?
It seems to get lost and covered
On the daily dreaded breath
Taking formality of battled stages
It's hard to maintain a focused position.
Point a view to points in you.

CULTURAL DIFFUSION

Water, the daughter
of Mother Nature

Creation gasping like
Everlasting breath control
Undergo experiments
Like past epidemics
Man-made played hate, like a game
Taught rules when school was out of session
Pressing chalked lines on the floor
Grown men drowned
Marked by devils on whatever level
Of discipline was imagined
Grabbing stable landmarks like you
Were beneath earth
Hurt
And pleasure is not too far off
Soft but hard
Digestible starved men
Some run from truth
I introduce conclusive answers

HOW TO SEND A MESSAGE WITHOUT SPEAKING

CONCRETE/PURE SOLID

Eye contact knocks out all noise & disturbances in my peripheral vision. 1 on 1 information exchanger. Stranger like kindness, just not in my case. Feeling out boobie traps like I'm in search of her G-spot. Boundaries currently now give me the silent treatment. Her body movement has a speech impediment because of intimate topics. We cop candyland fantasy strands and connect pieces of the puzzle. Previous abbreviated snippets lift, the closed curtains open. Coached in encroached closeness, inside voices spoken to the both of us. Hold tight of sexual sights that bite your memories like midnight flashes. Gashed up cuts and bruises healed up with reversed attentive actions. No need for off tempo clashes, we take a spin and work magnificently together. Top or bottom condom or stroll free. Verbal or surgical because when we undergo connections surgery is necessary. Behind closed doors different worlds are unimaginable by certain people. We seek sneak previews so fear doesn't capture amateur moments. Natural highs dive, divide or die if you sit & think about what should be. In the conclusive we strip open memories like track marks. To reach the root of school yard innocence with shadowed skin seen while stomachs are jumping like a trampoline. As little as holding hands and I would get motion sickness. Perfect pictures are no longer in existence.

WILLIE NAVARETTE SPITTING

I.
Plausible responses responsible for
tonsil maneuvered innuendoes below the
sheets we create slippery heat
steep inclines on the rise.
High tides glide surfaces with a purpose
motioned lips for I want to kiss.
Closeness in the direction to connection,
clenched tension where sensitive skins
relinquish liquids. Cooling heat created
by friction. Entrances collide til'
the slide inside no longer has a
need to stride. Climbed combined
obstacles traffic set aside like
it was optional. Colossal posture fossil
like meant to be intimacy, history in
the making. Retrieving the seizure like outbreak.
This occurrence was shown
as a token of appreciation.
Shook up from the waist down, now
lounging from the arousing insertion.
Services although nervousness
in the picture I need this
mixture in my flavor.

II.
My girlfriend I tend to
Imagine badgering me as a
Witness adjacent to 10 years
Down the road. Coded special
Format with satin sheets beneath the bed spread
Eligible for thrusts, pull suction works miracles.

My girlfriend I tend to
Imagine capturing the essence
Of beauty easily. Strike a pose
Clothes on or off.
I'm attentive to every last action. You're beautiful

Bundled up in winter clothes
Or nude under the sheets
Waiting anxiously

III.
Tongue twist lip mixed sexual
Grip. Nails underneath skin we
Begin to simmer in each other
Hot and heavy body weather
Crucial exploration can welcome
On any occasion, whether it be a walk
In the park or an unscheduled art form

IV.
From the music within I
Trim the fat from the exact
Measurements comprehension
Extensive but limited. Type twisted
Formulas pawned off on us.

V.
I WANT MORE
More than just bullshit.
Striving forward with
What you currently have.

VI.
Persona exposure I told her
To let loose and be vulnerable.
Paused in mid sentence because
Of certain contents like past boyfriends.
Instead I take a deep breath
And internalize her pain and gently
Say I understand cuz
I can relate to past issues. No need to
Prior engagement in vague territory.
I'll coax you like Maury's talk show.
The verbal has strength and stamina
The physical way may not be able
To endure. My touch will brush

Up against your skin like
Those pajamas that calm your
Nerves. Don't get me wrong,
I will serve you on multiple levels.

VII.
FREE WRITE
A handle on life like a
Wife and kids with money saved
Brave in the real world knocking
down walls for the family tree.
Pleasant heaven sent
she was present with such an aroma
I had to take hold of her.
A remedy steady.

VIII.
Sabotaged beliefs once you reach
The age of 13. Realizing your grave
Has been formed and ignored for the
Time being. But that is only because
You haven't fully been conceiving
The reasoning behind the format of life.
Spiced up countries because the U.S.
Is hungry to swallow blood whole.
Stolen goods, centuries old still on
Hold taken shape of older molds.
Concoct ingredients in the pot by
This greedy seamstress, we devour
Final products that are truly foreign objects.
We just don't care to dissect or
Reject presented ideas. Controlled like
Puppetry consecutively. Strings attached
To stay latched like lab rats.
Sexed up to connect to manhood,
We really misunderstood from the
primary watchings of Hollywood
Take it back to solid food, gradual upbringing
From naïve thinking to incompetencey
Deleted from human features preached

Incorrect teachings.
IX.
Trickery magician hat tricks
Gadget infantry up my sleeve.
Artillary useful in crucial
Abusive combat escalator status.

X.
WHY DO I LOVE TO WRITE?
I love to write so I
Can escape stagnation of
Condensed tension tossed in
Accumulative body bag prison.
The beginning of freedom
I couldn't conceive the weight lifted.
The gifted writtens felt like
A spiritual cleansing in reference to
Admission and acceptance of sins.

XI.
Once upon a time I stared
Spelling written rhymes to
Scribble lines from my mind.
My life sliced and diced time after
Time to catch up on my
past forgotten half. Slashed tires
so I had to roll out of bounds

XII.
How can you hold an angle
When you're tangled in pain
Though? Anger management has
a plan and placement for trading places

XIII.
A major problem to development
As we speak today escalate
Straight from the gangstas
that prank call the rap
Game to get paid.

XIV.
Change rearrange the
phase in life where I
just misunderstood the
type of cycle we as
Americans go through. Cut
Throat to the top until your best friend is patiently
Waiting to assassinate you.
Sniped off like washed
Away cloth, too many bloodstains
To stay in existence.
Resistance to punishment
Like an unseen corridor
Explored for fragments of freedom.
We seek humble outcomes but run into
No return of stern faces.

XV.
Baby
Sweetness
Mimi
Sugar
Chocolate Love
Connective tissue
Intermingled opposites attractive
Lip knot
Tongue touch
Blood flushed to the surface
Chocolate vanilla sandwich.

I twist words backwards
To have hidden double meanings.

When I lost my virginity
At the age of 16 was it meant for me?
What if I had waited for a female
True to me?
Would my views on life and women be differently?

REFLECTION (MOMS) 6/19/03

Family matters grow pain and get lost in the cause &
effect. Subjects that interrupt composed exposure through
formally known as Father & Mother. Love ain't the question but natural nutrition pertaining to parental up-bringing is the mission in which I'm seeking. Confusion
through positional misfortune forced intrusion in forms of
divorce papers. Stated truth produces the reason why Jesus
died crucified. Apparently in our coherent manners we
manage to defend our outer selves. Spell trust tough to
touch the grammar on that standard English noun. Now
I'm not accountable for the destruction stored in my kind
of war. Or shall I say, my kind of world that tickles your
toes or the arch between the teeth meeting the entrance
of the esophagus. Stop and listen Pops before I get caught
up in cops and robbers. Because if that happens then you
will really stop and become bitter. Mom, our communica-
tion level has gotten better. But this "men are evil" feeling
isn't soothing. Consider what I'm trying to sculpt and be.
My mixed diverse person looked at as not human has
emerged to stir chemicals making the wind fluster. Skirts
spin turning the term "special" into an instrument issued
by official cliques of 2. Drifted in mentioning phony
stories told to me while I'm in search for the real thing.
Meanwhile, my homies expressing the essence of pussy
and the magic a hot mouth and saliva can do to you.
I want a man's point of view, someone that has been
through a marriage or 2. Oh shit Dad, that's just like you.
Can you educate your only son to manhood? The Street's
word is helpful but the guidance has left their scrotum
hoping not to abort another one. On the run a quick fuck
is troublesome. Mumbled love to get in between panties
isn't the route I plan to go about.

WILLIE NAVARETTE

MY NAME IS PEARL SADE QUICK

I was born in Harlem Hospital 135th street on the west side, before Harlem Hospital got clean, where rats were landlords and the roaches paid rent. I grew up where roots were shown and I stood short and round like a bush on the side of the street. February 6th, 1987 my eyes saw like a prize, the life ahead.

From that moment on my life has been a battle, a struggle, a trial after trial, tribulation after tribulation, never a moment's rest. I have always been a soldier without knowing it. I'm the girl in the mirror who always wanted to be, like a poem I wrote, I envy the girl in the mirror, so like me, but she lives a perfect life. I'm a girl who tries her best to become a part of a better life.

In this world poetry is my life and I didn't know if it was reality or an illusion. I see myself with future experiences, learning with every rhyme and every song. My poetry will become a long song of my unforgettable past and the memorable future of the family I will have made. My life consists of what I know I'll accomplish because of the smart and zealous person I am, I am beautiful. I am future. I am, like Joe says, forever will BE POETRY.

BLACK HISTORY
MAN, I REMEMBER

When I was little
I wanted to be different.
I wanted to be Spanish
Because I loved the way they spoke,
Or an Indian
Because they had purity and beauty,
Or White
Because I believed, when I was little,
That they lived better.

No, because as I grew up
I realized being the nationality
And skin color that I am
Means strength, courage,
Persistence, triumph.
I am all who fought before me
Because in my blood is a
Creator, a thinker, a future
A tradition holder.
My skin represents a certain struggle,
A fighter lies within me,
A natural will to never, ever give up
Like all those who came before me.

I BLAMED YOU

You with legs wide apart, awaiting the innocent.
The smarts not there.

You with a child and now a disease which you have
now passed down to her.

With tears and learning about your disease you realized
you had HIV. You gave it to her.

Liquids and pills she has to take. A date was set.
She wouldn't live to 11.

(February 11th was her 11th birthday)

I blamed you for not understanding.

Your mistakes keep her confined in a prison
of no sleep-overs

And specialized camps for people like her.

You made it so that she cries because she's different.

Then you turn around and make it so that I feel bad, a
responsibility that *you* gave to me.

I didn't give her the poison that lives in her blood. You did.

You gave her a sentence date. I wish it was me instead of her.

I blamed you for not thinking, for putting yourself and
her through this.

I love my sister.

I blamed you and I think I still do.

I think I'd switch places with both of you. But I can't.

I wish you would have been more responsible in the
decisions that affected you, her, me.

NATURAL WORLD

The nature of waterfalls
Finally the wind blew past
Baby born
Life in the form of just beginning trees
Never before leaves

Water splashes over history.
Danger brings new beginnings for plants of chance.
Peaceful patterns, beautiful trees
Bounce off water, which reflects life.
Browns   blues   whites.
I feel as though I'm painting
Brush strokes of blues, browns, whites, greens.
No other thing, person or place
Can look so breathtaking
Doing nothing besides doing what it does.

Naturally

I imagine painters of love and life.
It swims off deep penetration
beneath its beautiful surface.
The sun is blinded
By beautiful nimbus clouds of flat bottoms and fluffy tops.
Then, as it was meant to be, the sun shines once more
Breathtaking, heat blazing as before.

With every part of nature there is reflection
I feel as though I have changed
I just want to
Do me
Be me
Be free.
I want to remember what it was like to do things

To make me happy whole-heartedly
Without anyone's approval
I am nature because this is where no matter what trials
Or tribulations it never speaks against you.
Nor is it ever judgmental
It's unlike Bronx concrete.
It adjusts with my every step

MONTH'S RENT

Walls fall around me
There's nothing I can do.
Broken windows,
Broken doors, falling cabinets
Overdue bills, as I walk
I feel the pressure.

Someone's calling.
Cable man, smart energy phone lady,
Landlord, last month's rent overdue

My angry mother goes to court,
Tries to give the judge a clear picture.
Full of pain through her tired eyes,
Tears drop.
Moaning from the landlord,
Talks shit but doesn't
Live where we live.

PEACE

Peace only lives in fairytales of
Three little pigs and Little Red Riding Hood
On the way to grandma's house and
I'll huff and I'll puff and
I'll blow your house down…
Peace is war.
How can peace ever be real
When every day we demand it,
We fight for it?
Isn't that when peace blurs?
Where it blurs into the concrete of
Blood, sweat and tears,
Dead bodies and fears
Of those who only know how to
Fight for their right to survive.
Peace has become
By any means necessary
We live by
The right to bear arms
I talked to myself the other day and thought,
If this is what peace is then what is violence?
Because everyday one of our soldiers
Dies for peace
Suicide bombers
Die for peace
When will peace mean just that,
Peace?
I have cried for small children
Who have lost their parents over
Peace
And this is supposed to mean
We are safe and harmless, without hatred.
But all the peace we know is death,
Fight.

By any means necessary
Peace is lost in the mouths of our
Most idiotic dictators.
We are fighting to create a
Peaceful place for all the children to live.
But we send our young away to fight for peace.
We get back a flag draped box.
Is this what we had in mind?

So when you say peace
I say Where?
Peace surely does not lie in the
Badges of crooked cops who sell and smoke
The shit they seize,
Blackmail to get what they want
And put away the minorities
And overlook the majority
Who kill and blame
Peace.

So when you find peace
Tell me...
Peace was not in the front of my building
Last night when there was another killing
Of another father, brother, mother
Selling explicit shit that kills the mind.
Peace was not in the mother's mind as she
Killed her child because she couldn't
Handle the responsibility.
Peace to me is a five letter word.
Peace is death in a pretty wrapper.
Peace.
When you find the real meaning
Tell me.

WHY I WRITE

PEARL QUICK, POWER WRITER
NOVEMBER 8, 2003

I scream onto my pages knowing
It can't talk back, writing to escape my world.

I live in a world filled with
Drug dealers and crackheads
And I'd rather create a new world
Better than my own,
I feel free to write and make
Up a world far better in comparison
To my reality.

This is where I live and breathe
And for me to write another world
So inciting that when you
Stop you swear you were
Just watching a movie. Then
That's why I write.
Desire is that heat that makes
Your hair stand on end. That's
What I feel when I write
About the world I live in.
I live in a harsh reality and
It's hard for me to talk about it so
I write about the Hood because
The character I make up
Has to go through it and
For one moment..or 212 moments
I don't have to.

PEARL QUICK

getting healed.
It's crazy!, how a perso
the advantages by; bre
ing up; (say slowly).
So, here comes the sour
the peal, that's pealing,
simultaneously, give
tons of loud pealed, s
By I everyday shower
Being hereby, as I will
get vanquished near
keeping my eye on you
franchising on amendm
send for more blotteri
You been greedy, running
and not even getting
greeted
So, why keep gatherin
All these non-senses;
repeating, or it alway
repeated.

SYESHA SANTOS

ANXIOUS TO BREAK LOOSE

Don't give a fuck
Whether I win or lose.
I live life in an inner cage
Always full of rage
Cause I know
I haven't committed a crime
For which,
My time on earth should be miserable.
Time after time,
I question my being.
Why is my life
So not worth living?
I try to form a good impression
Through a smile, make-up,
Dressy clothes.
I hide my depression.
But I cry,
And have attempted suicide
Like anyone else who's afraid to admit it.
Anger has caused me to punch walls,
Crawl on the floor
Like a child,
Through the empty halls,
When no one is around
Lock myself in my room,
Rock back and forth
To that tune,
Talk to myself,
Destroy my heath
Because I'm locked in an inner cage.
Full of rage.
But they say,
"It's just a phase"
that I feel this way because of my age.
But as I turn the pages of my endless life story

It's hard to read what was good and glory.
Why is it
That I loved the world so much?
Once I'm betrayed
It feels like a really bad punch.
Never knew life would be so hard
But all I know is
Teary eyes and a soul full of scars.
I try to depart from pain and sadness,
But it turns ten times stronger.
I feel like I'm stuck at the border
Of regression and depression
But I have yet to learn my lesson,
Because I return to the same shit over and over again.
Pain is my friend.

MEAN

I mean
Mean actions
Actions are taken
Taken far
Far and lost
Lost are my thoughts
Thoughts within
Within my mind
Mind out of control
Control is what I don't have
Have you seen
Seen and not said
Said a word
Word is only one
One word said is enough
Enough to go crazy
Crazy insane
Insane taken away
Away is happiness
Happiness is a new start
New start of stability

TWIN TOWERS
9.1.2002

No matter your age or race,
We were united as one in grief.
No matter where you were from,
Silence was in the wind,
Souls and spirits wandered free.
Unbearable, hard to believe.
Even if you're not the emotional type,
You felt the pain.
Nothing will ever be the same.
The day after
People wanted to hide,
No one could find joy,
Everyone felt the deep void.

A year has passed.
To tell you the truth,
If you mention it
The exact feeling will present itself
Because it wasn't an act of greed,
It was an act of hate.
So many people died.
The ones who witnessed this tragedy cried.
Some lost brothers, mothers, lovers.
Bin laden believed he could tear the nation apart.
He believed wrong.
It was just a new start.
The souls in heaven,
Or the spirits that soar around
Would not want their families, their friends
To cry or frown.
So please move on,
Don't forget.
But please don't live a life of torment and regret.

I AM

I am,
I am no longer a child
I see,
I see the truth
About,
About what you did to me.
You chose addiction over our family.
You left me stranded and confused,
Secluded from my childhood,
Worrying about you.
In my mind it was okay.
Today
I don't feel the same
I was a child who needed her birth mother.
I grew up without my blood brother.
In your mind everything is fine,
'cause you did your time.
Every time I cry
I try to forget.
I find myself tormented by regrets.
There is nothing you could ever say
To change my feelings.
You were wrong
And there is no healing.

SYESHA DANIELLE SANTOS

thing healed
it's crazy, how a person-
he advantages by, "brew
g 🔳 up, (say slowly).

here comes the sounds
repeal, that's pealing, o
multaneously, give ou
ns of loud pealed, mou
everyday showerin
ing hereby, as I will no
et vanquished, nearlie
eeping my eye on you,
anchising an amendmen
end for more blottering
been greedy, running a
not even getting th
reeted
why keep gathering,
these non-senses, you
peating, or it always
repeated

NEW JACKS

Karina Cordero

Aleyva Guzman

Kristine Massa

Arline Hernandez

Manuel Murray

Madeline Iglesias

Anthony Pittman

Jennifer Kahn

Danielle Pollard

Robbin Keys

Catalina Puente

Amanda Maisonet

Yaritza Rodriguez

Jonathan Maldonado

Karina Sanchez

Dorian Sanders

KARINA CORDERO

Who am I?

I'm the girl who used to get teased.

I'm the person who goes through things in life.

I'm the girl who's shy once in a blue

But now I'm the girl that gets treated nice for

Who she is.

I'm the girl that learned how to love herself for who
she is

And not for what people see or say.

I, I am the 5'4 girl, with dirty blond hair, not fat but not
skinny and sometimes a frown a smile.

I am, and will always be the crazy girl who had to learn
how to except her self for who and how she is, and how
she looks

Learning not to listen to people to what people say but
what I say.

I'm that girl who you will know and count on anytime
and anywhere!!!!!!!!!

Y Que?

Looking around and seeing how others are treated,

Just because I'm this color, does it matter?

Why is it a problem if I'm Dominican black or Chinese?

Does it matter if I'm Spanish?

People suffering because of their skin color.

Being black!!! Is it a problem? I think not!

Why do you find him, her or them so different?

Why do right have to be right? And black in the back?

Does that sound right at all? I think not

Why are we races?

Being races is part of the world.

But should it be here? (Huh) answer me

And it better be I think not!

People that are races don't realize that they are dehuman-
izing themselves

Don't they notice that it don't matter if I get married to a black person.

I was raised by Dominicans; I hear the raises all the time.

Why must you be that way?

That's a question you, them and me ask.

Nobody knows the answer.

I know I'm tan and for some I might be whack. But guess what, I might be black!!

But did you care? Hell No!

You were to busy looking at my skin color, and soon assuming I'm Hispanic.

Assuming (huh) get it you making an ass out of you're selves

But yeah I'm Hispanic Y QUE??? And WHAT?

If I want I could be black and proud, Y QUE?? Tell me something now!!!

The only Death

Looking straight at him. Still thinking he's here. Seeing him and hearing his breathing. My eyes and me can't take it, we can't believe it.

Why can't I see it?

Why can't I take it? Those warm hugs you use to give me. Those courageous words you use to say.

I or should I say we never thought it would happen like this.

The phone rings… I wonder who it is?

As I hear those words " HAYYY KARI LLA NO HAY PAPA!"

I slowly drop the phone and as I go down slowly all you hear is my dad on the phone " hello Kari, Kari…."

I start crying, still not believing he's gone, refusing the consequences.

Thinking that my friend, my protector and my love is now gone to a zone I would never see him in.

WHY THE FUCK DID YOU LEAVE ME?????

DID I DO SOMETHING?

PLEASE DON'T LEAVE ME ALONE!

Is to late now! What can I do?
All my love and affection has all left with you.
I'll make sure you take my soul and maybe even me with you,
You dying is like me dying, no more Kari no more world.
HOW DARE YOU LEAVE ME ALONE?
Is hopeless now,
But hahaha! I know you alive and you'll always be alive in my heart and in my eyes.
R.I.P
MY DAD, MY SOUL, MY PROTECTOR, MY GRAND FATHER, MY PAPA!

HURT
As I enter the house I see everybody surrounding me. As I look in his eyes and explain, but don't be leave or want to her what I have to say.
My lies or my truth don't want to be heard.
As I walk towards my room, keep hearing the screaming, as I slam the door I hear the footsteps. Door slams open, and eyes staring at me. Words coming out of my mouth that weren't meant to be said, but already out in the air. Those words.
All of a sudden I'm in the floor.
As I'm in that dark corner all crunched up, I feel the burning sensation going through my skin, as I yell those words "please stop" my defender and at that moment my only family stops the abuse.
I stay on the floor crying like never before.
But as I think about it all I have to say is that people that treat others like animals they should know that PAY BACK IS A BITCH!

Anger

Sitting down, rocking back and forth, my fist closed
and tears coming down my face.
I start screaming,
breaking the glass on top of the furniture.
As I see the bottle dropping and breaking,
I sit on my bed taking my hands and covering my face.
I start crying and the words
"Why me?" coming out of my mouth
As I sit in the middle of the bed crouching back and
forth, I start to think
"Why do I get treated so different?"
"Why can't they understand me?"
"What have I done to them?"
I stop crying and I look at myself in the mirror,
I clean my face and stop shedding all these tears cause
they're not worth it.
Than I lie on my bed and fall asleep until a new day
comes
Which is tomorrow!!

WASN'T AS GOOD AS IT SEEMED

Life wasn't always as good as it seems

I use to shed a tear every night for the simple fact that I use to get picked on. People never gave me a chance. How dare they treat me like trash with out knowing how I act? They judged me of how I looked. Just because I was fat doesn't mean I had no feelings. I have a friend that stood by me. She was always with me in the good time and bad times. Now I look better, and the people that use to tease me don't remember me. I feel proud of all the things I accomplished in life. Now guys look at me and say Daaaaammmmm with out knowing how much I worked to get here.

Now I look at people and I say in my mind, " hell yeah, you better look at me, I didn't loose 75 pounds for you just to stand there and don't stare at this gorgeous girl standing right beside you!!!"

KARINA CORDERO

ALEYVA GUZMAN

FEELING ALONE

This feeling I get sometimes I don't know why it comes

I feel as if no one cares about me. Like if I'm a no one when this feeling comes I cry myself to sleep

And I stay quiet during the day. This is something that makes me wonder is there something missing in me? Is it because my father is gone? Is it because he doesn't call me just to say hi? That could be it, because it hurts me a lot to know that he's still alive and he knows where to find me. Or is it because I'm scared that I won't accomplish my goals. Scared that I might be alone in the future and lose everyone I love? But I won't know until the day comes. And as soon as I find out I'll let you know, because maybe you can relate to this feeling. And if you do I won't feel alone anymore.

DO YOU?

It has been six years
and now you come.
When you look at me
what do you see?
Do you look at me
as your daughter or
just any human being?
I've always wondered,
Do I have a father?
Is he alive or dead?
Does he know I exist?
Does my name run
through his head?
Does he think $100
stops my pain?
He's real funny,
that's what drives me
insane.

I hear all these kids that
live with or see
their fathers and
this is all they know
how to say:
"I hate my father.
I wish he would die."
I think then,
You're lucky you even
got a dad.
Do you know
all the people that
don't have one and
wish they did?
Well I do, because
I'm one of them.
I hate it how he never
calls,
how he doesn't help my
mother,
how he's never there.
So to those with a
Father that you talk to
or live with,
cherish him.
Before he is gone.

MADELINE

M mysterious
A although she's loud
D doesn't take shit from no one
E enjoys life itself
L lives life to the fullest
I intelligent girl
N nothing can stop her from doing what she does
E enthusiastic about a lot of things.

WHAT POWER WRITING MEANS TO ME

A door that was opened to me
Something that helped expand my mind
Recommended to me by a good friend
A place where respect is all around
Where you can express yourself
and everyone's opinion
makes you want to write more
So I want to thank Joe
For opening this door
And I want to thank Amy
and Roland because when
they give me an opinion
they encourage me to
Write More!

YOU

This is to you
No one else
But you
Just you, you
And only you
I want to write
All about you
Not this or that
Just you
Because you
Are you
Unique
And quiet.
But there's one question
Before I keep writing
About you.
Who are you?

SEARCHING

I'm looking for something
But I don't know what
It is
I don't know where
To start the search
I hope I' ll find it
Soon
Maybe someone
Would give me a clue
But until then my
Search will continue

Getting healed.

It's crazy, how a perso[n]
the advantages by; bre[ak]
ing up; (say slowly).
So, here comes the sou[nd]
the peal, that's pealing
simultaneously, give
tons of loud pealed, s[o]
By I, everyday shower
Being hereby, as I will
get vanquished, near[ly]
keeping my eye on you[r]
franchising on amendm[ent]
send for more blotter[y]
You been greedy, running
and not even getting
greeted
So, why keep gatherin[g]
All these non-senses,
repeating, or it alwa[ys]
repeated.

ARLINE HERNANDEZ

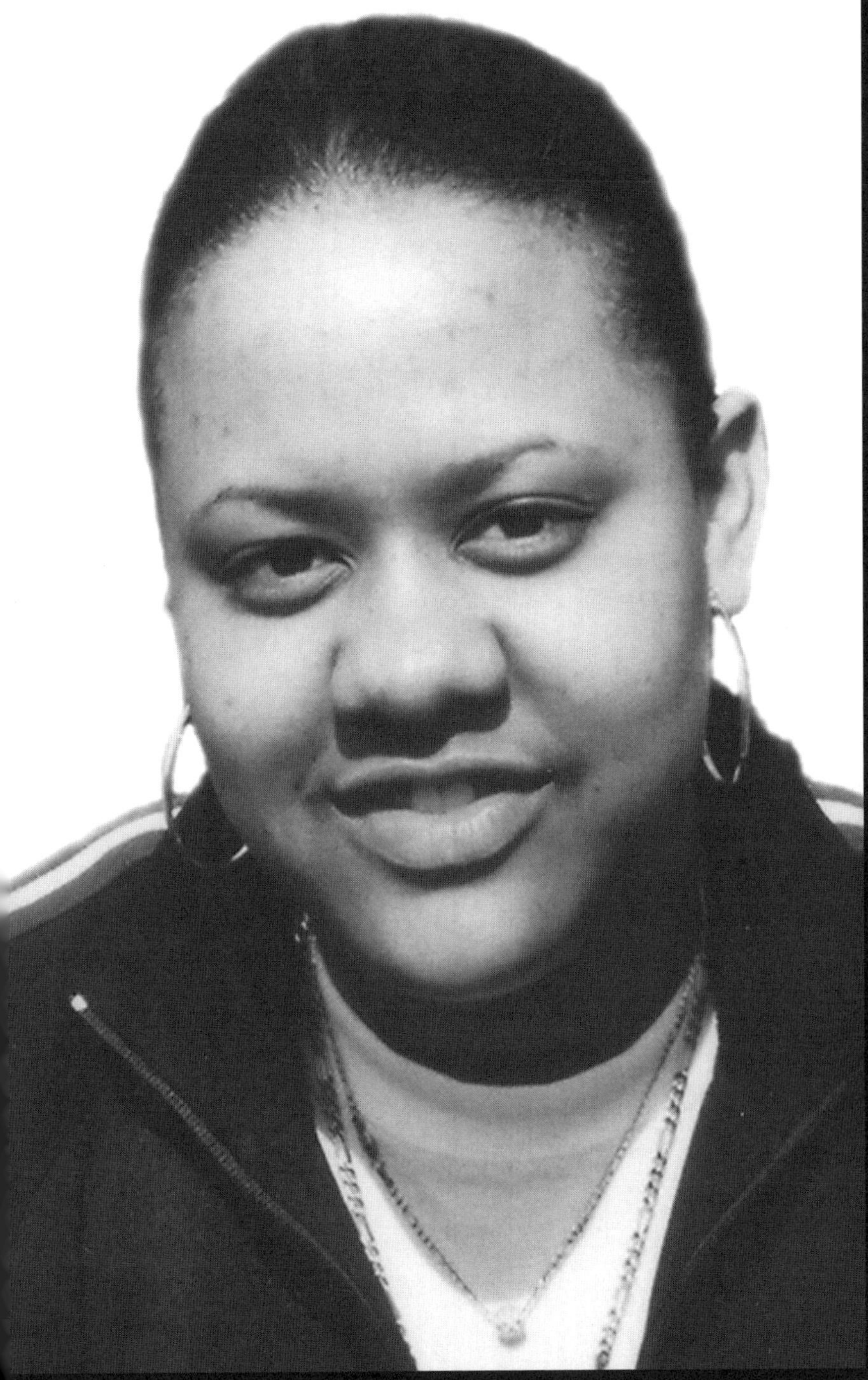

MY GHETTO

Raised with pain and fed nothing but dreams

The ghetto, the kind of place where you go to dream
And dreams are nothing but sheets of paper
you take with you to the bodega
Where dreams are having the hottest rides
and being the biggest
Most feared rug dealer in all the Bronx

The ghetto, my ghetto is where only the strong survive
And even when you have survived you have failed.

Raised with pain and fed nothing but dreams
The ghetto is the only place he wants to be
He is the man that is seeking his cause
But he's waiting for opportunity to come
 knock, knockety, knock on his door.

Yeah, he survived,
The shootouts and the gang fights
He dropped out of high school,
Skipped class to go smoke with his boys
He wanted to be a rapper and host rap battles and shit
Funny thing is, he's 36 years old now
And doing nothing but the streets.

Raised with pain and fed nothing but dreams
The ghetto is the only place that he wants to be,
Where he wants to be.

THE RISE

Shatter, Shatter, Shatter
Is the sound that my soul
Makes when it is sad and broken.
Shatter, shatter, shatter
Is the way my heart sounds
When its truth has not been spoken.

Spoken truly as the sound
Of birds chirping on a
Morning summer breeze
Spoken freely and walking
Down a street with a mighty cool ease.

Whispering beyond my
Many mountains of thought
Whispering inside for the endless
War that has not been fought.

For the children that cry out
But don't say a word
For the people that have spoken
But have not been heard.

Listen to the inner beauty
That lies upon you.
Listen to the souls of the people
And the wisdom within you.

WIFE BEATER

He got that cute girl he be wifin'
He loves her so much,
He hits her with his fists like lightning

He literally knocks you off your feet
When you're tired of everything
You wake up the next morning
With a swollen eye as you cry
He hears your sobs
And makes love to you better than the night before.

Dizzy stars and birds roam around your head
animation style
I take you out to have fun but you barely crack a smile

He got that cute girl he be wifin'
He loves her so much
He hits her with his fists like lightning

"But he loves me," you say in his defense
But sweetie, stupidity isn't the best defense,
Neither is ignorance

He rapes you after you refuse make love to him
He does it harder and harder
As your tears stream down the side of your face
Like holy water
As you pray to God to please make him stop.

You pray for your life to be
Taken away from this Earth
But God refuses to listen

As he finishes, he wipes his sweat
And kisses your unloving mouth.
With a smirk he whispers in your ear,
"Baby, you know I love you"

He got that cute girl he be wifin'
He loves her so much
He hits her with his fists like lightning

He pounds on your body
As if practicing for his next match
But he doesn't realize that you are the best catch
He told me he wouldn't do it anymore
"Hey girls, it doesn't feel as bad as it looks" you say

Damn girl, I feel so much for you
I hope you find your right of way
Because on this day
You don't want my help.
But I guess that's what I get
For trying to be a caring friend.
And even though you rejected me
I'll still be there for you in the end.
I LOVE YOU!

ARLINE HERNANDEZ

getting healed.
It's crazy, how a perso
the advantages by, bre
ing up, (say slowly).
So, here comes the sou
the peal, that's pealin
simultaneously, give
tons of loud pealed s
By I everyday shower
Being hereby, as I will
get vanquished near
keeping my eye on you
franchising on amendm
send for more blotteri
You been greedy, running
and not even getting
greeted
So, why keep gatherin
All these non-senses,
repeating, or it alway
repeated.

MADELINE IGLESIAS

WHEN U

When U look at me I…stop
When U look at me I stare back
When U look at me I think
That U are going to say something to me
When I look at U I blush scarlet

When U talk to me I…stop
When U talk to me I respond back
When U talk to me I think
That U are going to say something romantic…But
What U say is "How U goin' Maddy?"
When U talk to me I blush crimson

When U kiss me I don't stop
When U kiss me I kiss back
When U kiss me I feel the passion
U have for me and I have for U
But when you left me I couldn't look back
When U left me I blushed blue

When U.

MADELINE IGLESIAS

KENYA JONES

COVERED IN CHOCOLATE

I am a young teen and sweet as can be
My innocence is shattered but can be
Covered by celibacy

Covered in chocolate is the
Color of my skin,
My flesh is the color of berries
Cratered with scars and filled with wisdom

I stand as Kenya Shauntiea Jones
Born of the year 1986.
I shall not hide who I am
My burdens and worries will outlive who I am.

So what that I'm loud
I tell the world I am here to be heard
I have a powerful voice
Filled with many tales

Because I am covered in chocolate
People underestimate me
They presume I'm a chick full of rhythm,
Illiterate to society and think it revolves around me

I am also a poet
I take my thoughts
And my song and
I sing my life onto paper.

DANCE WITH ME

We missed out on a lot of years
We haven't spoken in almost 10 years
I try to ignore the fact that you disappeared
Walked out on the family
And never cared
But I forgave because if
You are gone 2day or 2morrow
You will still be my father.

Today is my special day
And I am honored that you came
I ask that you take moment and
Dance with me

If this is the last time I see you
I can say that I had my dance
The most important dance in my life
Sweet 16 father and daughter dance
The first dance of the night

GOOD NIGHT

Gave away another day
Missing your voice, your smile and
The things you say
But I will not mourn nor cry
I will celebrate a new life
A life of my peace.
As I stand over you, I release my burden
Finally my questions will be answered
Unfortunately, never answered in words
Now we are face to face, still I converse with myself.
I hope you liked the last day we met
Your eyes closed, laid out on a bed,
How bad can that be
I shall use this as my strength
Giving my flesh the ability to hate,
My heart the ability to bleed
Because of you now I get to sleep.
Good night

KENYA JONES

ENNIFER KAHN

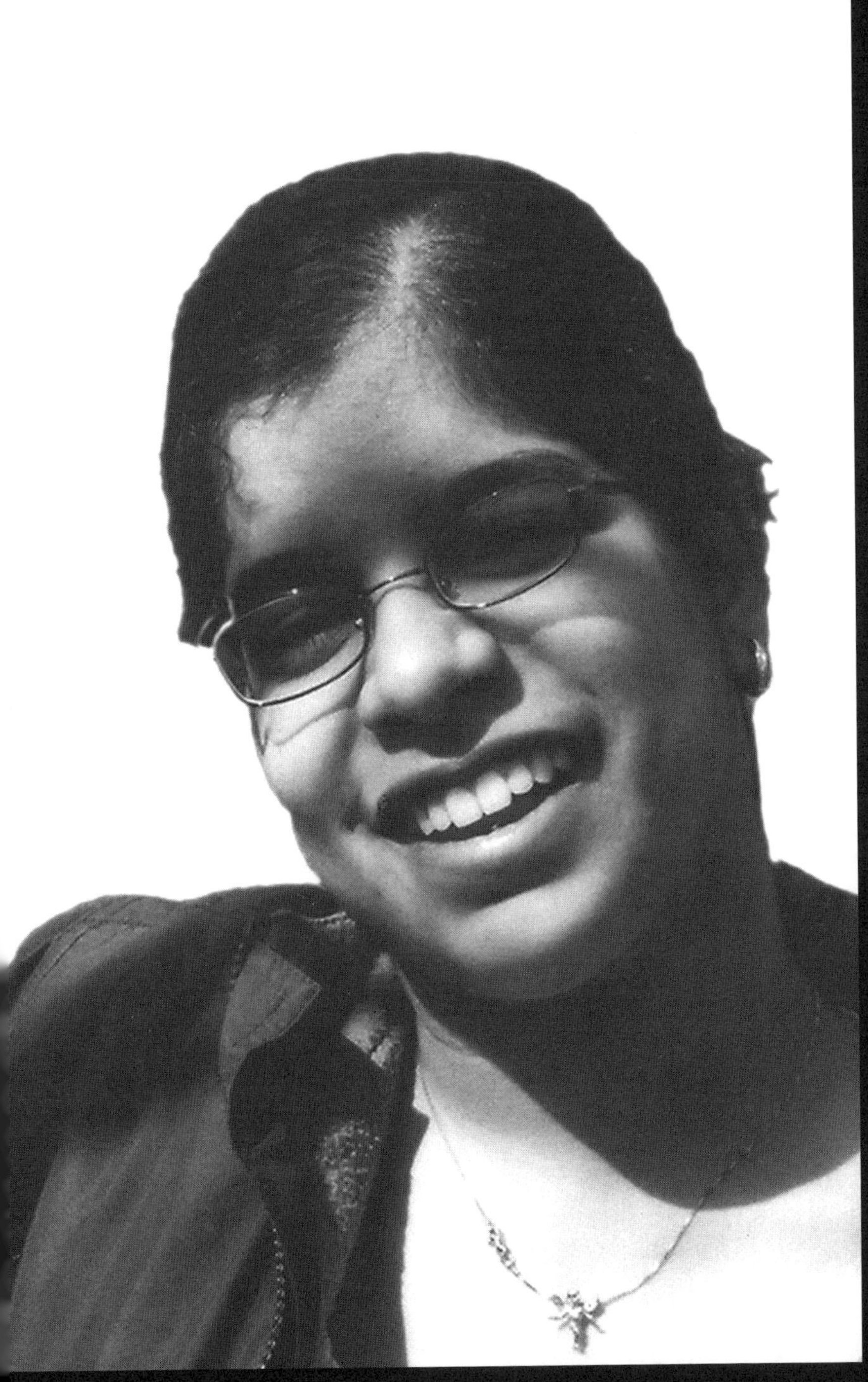

POWER WRITING

What has power writing meant to me? Power Writing has opened my eyes to life. It has opened my eyes to things I never thought of. It makes me disappear into a world that was never known to me. Writing makes me have mixed emotions. It makes me laugh. It makes me cry. It makes me have feelings that confuse me. It makes me so confused that the way I feel about writing in unknown to me. Writing has made me a better person. Writing makes me want to keep searching for the meaning of life. Writing has helped me express myself in a more positive way. Without Power Writing I don't think I would have become a better person. Power Writing stayed true to its name because it has been so powerful that it has impacted my life so very deeply.

I AM SICK AND TIRED

I am sick & tired
of sickness.
I am sick & tired
Of waiting
every day for the phone to ring
full of bad news.
I am sick & tired
Of hearing I am scheduled
For my next surgery on…
My life is the hospital.
I am sick & tired
of the extra weight
that drags me along.
I am sick & tired
of knowing that I cannot do something
without my mother freaking out.
I am sick & tired
of not knowing the many outcomes
that await me, wishing &
praying that at least
one call will bring good news.
I am sick & tired
of feeling like a baby.
I am sick & tired
of knowing I am sick
and the world still does not know
that I am proud
to be a fighter.
I am proud to be me.

WHY DO I WRITE?

I write because
it makes me crazy.
When I write I write all sorts of craziness
I write because
it has changed me.
I write because
I love to write.
And writing loves me.
Writing has helped me realize my family's pain.
I write because
I realized that I had so many unspoken words,
Words that are very hard to say.
Writing has changed my vision of the world
Writing has adopted my soul.
When I write my mind escapes me.
Writing has made me not want to be noticed
Because I am noticed only in those eyes
That want to notice me.
I write because
I am not a writer, but
I am the words that I write.

JENNIFER KAHN

ROBBIN KEYS

GONE

It's not a shoot out
It's not a fight
It's not a raping
Or a stabbing someone thought
Was out of sight
It was the death of my closest friend
The way she took her last breath
And as I watched her body
Life and death
Watching her beautiful brown skin turn
From a beautiful chocolate brown
To pale brown
Holding her warm hand just for it
To turn ice cold
Watching as everyone cried in sympathy
And/or pain
No longer hearing a sound but
I can see the tears running down the faces
Of her relatives
One last look and the room starts spinning
The look on her face suddenly shows all the pain
She's been through
And the release from it all
Death
What does it mean?
The worst death I'd ever seen
Not a lynching
Not a flesh eating disease
But it was my Grandma
Suffering and dying at ease
That was the worst death I'd ever seen
But it seems just like yesterday I was sitting by your side
It seems just like 3 hours ago you were saying everything
Would be alright

It seems like yesterday
We were laughing together
It feels like yesterday you picked me up from school
After I had a fake asthma attack
Just so I could spend time with you
But this pain I feel
It feels like just yesterday that you died
Since you've been gone
I've stopped believing in myself
Since you've been gone
The sight of your picture paralyzes my heart
For days cuz you're gone
And since you've been gone
Mom's gone crazy and Benjamin had another baby
Whitney's losing her straight A's
And I've missed school for several days
Robert's a drop and
Phillip is like a madman running about
I remember when you were here
The calmness and spiritual surroundings
The curfews and the month-long groundings
Since you left we lost all control
Of our own lives
A lot has really changed now that you are
Gone.

MAY 16TH
BIRTHDAY

My eyes opened to tall people wearing white & blue.
Grew up in a crack-headed, broken down building,
every Friday night sleeping on the floor for the same
routine, a shootout.
I'm fifteen years old now and I still dream about being
a kid again,
being teased because I'm mixed cultured with mixed
emotions.
To get out of this painful world I turn on my Sean Paul
CD to #10,
singing along with it
"I'm still in love with you boy."

Robbin Elizabeth Keys, turn that shit down!"
My mother yells.
So I run outside to my courtyard where I see the lady
upstairs begging
for a quarter to buy a loosie.

This is a lost world
I am lost in it as well.

YOU HELPED ME

When you were here
I always leaned on your shoulders for support
You were always so strong mentally and physically
You put my problems by yours
I used to see your death as nothing but pain & heartache
But now I see it as you helping me to walk
Now that you're not here
I have no shoulders to lean on
And I have started to crawl through broken streets
Covered in glass and crack needles
But now I'm walking
Yet I still stumble through the cracks in the ground
And the uneven sidewalks
You helped me to see
What I needed to see when you died
You taught me to walk on my own
You helped me.

ROBBIN KEYS

getting healed
It's crazy, how a pers
the advantages by, bre
ing ~~up~~ ups (say slowly).
So, here comes the sou
the peal, that's pealing
Simultaneously, give
tons of loud pealed, s
By I everyday shower
Being hereby, as I will
get vanquished near
keeping my eye on yo
franchising on amendm
send for more blotter
You been greedy, running
and not even getting
greeted
So, why keep gatherin
All these Non-senses,
repeating, or it alway
repeated.

AMANDA MAISONET

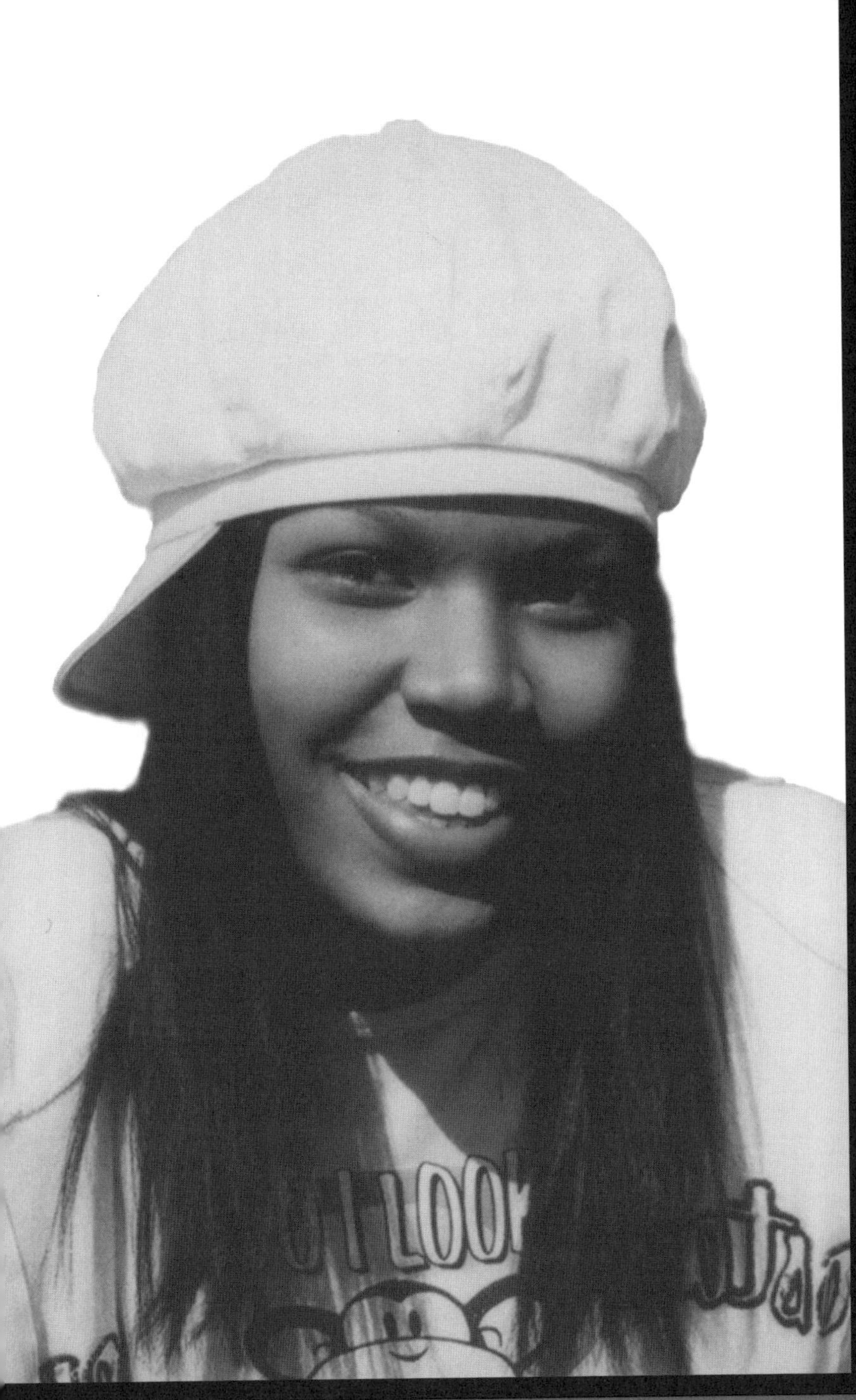

"DEATH OF A BROTHER"

Dedicated to Raymond

Crying a little every night
Smiling a little every morning
Knowing that you're in a safe place
Yet knowing that there's no way to reach you.
Here thinking that you forgot about us when you didn't,
Finding out that you loved us and missed us.
There you were thinking the same thing,
But will you ever know the truth?
Knowing from the start how beautiful a person you were,
But never having a chance of knowing you.
Wishing that I could hold your hand,
Wishing that I could hear the kiss from you in my ear,
Wishing that I could feel your so called nappy hair in
my hands,
Wishing that I could smell your favorite cologne,
Wishing that I could get one, just one, more chance
with you.
I know you think your brother Marcos is mad at you,
But deep down I know he's messed up
I know your baby sister Melody was your favorite.
You had your reasons.
She cries every time she remembers that.
I know you think Mami didn't love you but you were
her first baby,
She was just tired of only getting calls about you being
in trouble.
I don't know what you thought of me,
I guess I was always the quiet girl.
I know you loved me,
I know you missed me
But how can I ever go on without knowing that you
know the truth?

We loved you Raymond, we truly did.
But here we were thinking that you forgot about us when
you didn't,
Finding out that you loved us and missed us.
There you were thinking the same thing
But will you ever know the truth?

10 YEARS FROM NOW

It's amazing how far I came.
In just a blink of an eye,
I got everything I dreamed of.

I'm an independent woman
Looking out for myself
Paying my own bills
Living on my own.

I look back and remember those times
When I sat in class waiting, just waiting to get out of my
daily routine,
Waking up in the morning not even wanting to get out
of bed,
Asking my parents for money so that I can go shopping.

Now here I am world
Getting the things I worked my a** for.
My own successful business,
My own crib,
My hot ride.

Giving back to the place
That made it possible for me to even dream,
Giving back to the people
Who gave me strength and told me anything is possible
as long as you work hard for it.

I watched the world around me and how much it
changed,
I watched people come in and out of my life,
But I still and always will have those people
who got my back
and pushed me along the way,

while I pushed them in the right direction,
watching them grow into professionals and admiring
them, loving them.

They are my backbone now and forever,
I thank them
But more importantly I thank myself.

THAT THING YOU DO

\ Why are you looking at me?
Is there something you have to say?
Do you have something on your mind?
Cuz your stare is really bothering me.
Your frantic eyes and rhythmic blinking,
I can't stand them.
The way your nose turns red when you're cold,
The way your top lip curls when you smile,
Even the look on your face when you see one of your
friends.

Damn I can't stand you
The way you talk,
The way you walk,
And the way you say hi to your boys.

And now there you are
In the place where I can go
And not have to see you
The place I call home
Sitting there where I sat,
Eating the food that I ate,
Talking to the person who I was just with.
What do you want?
I can tell you what I want.
I want you to want me the way I want you,
I want you to understand the sh*t my heart feels for you,
I want you to understand the things I'm going through,
But in the end it all starts with you.

Damn I gotta have you,
The way you talk,
The way you walk,
And the way you say hi to your boys.

So why are you looking at me?
Do you have something to say?
Cuz just you looking at me give me chills.
Your lovely eyes and sexy lips,
I love them.
The way your nose turns red when you're cold,
The way you top lip curl when you smile,
Even the look on your face when you see one of your
friends.

Damn I just love you,
The way you talk,
The way you walk,
And the way you say hi to your boys.

AMANDA MAISONET

getting heated.
It's crazy, how a pers
the advantages by, bre
ing ~~○~~ up? (say slowly).
so, here comes the sou
the peal, that's pealin
simultaneously, give
tons of loud peated, s
By ≠ everyday shower
Being nereby, as ≠ will
get vanquished near
keeping my eye on yo
franchising on amendm
send for more blotter
You been greedy, running
and not even getting
greeted.
So, why keep gatherin
All these non-senses,
repeating, or it always
repeated.

ONATHAN MALDONADO

J comes back and he blazes again. A couple of shots couldn't take 'em and now he's at it again! Does the gun I hold make me more of a man? The streets done taught me all of the Game! Scarface once told me the world was coming to an end! This life ain't promising so I'm clearin' my sins! At times my niggaz get me rollin' again! Nigga I ain't cock-blockin' but I'm doin' my endz! I'll love every single bitch that came wit' u on my dick! I don't mean to sound conceited, but this is telekinesis! I'm lyrically inclined but mentally confined! "D" stated white lines n I would die for my crimes! U don't have a choice but to love it or hate it! Enter my matrix…I'm not Neo but I'm nearly makin' U think on how the matrix system works!

MY AMBITIONZ AZ A WRITAH

My ambitionz as a writah…helps me relieve
The stress from the streets! I write to make
U think. I love to see everyone moved
From my sins! It shows they unda'stand
A lil' the kinda world I'm from! Now
Listen to me because…it's on, 'cause I
Speak the truth and 'cause I said so! Look
At ya payin' attention to what I say, waitin'
Anticipatin' my every move…But let me
Fill U in on this paranoial mind of mine -
The cops wanna see this almighty King d-ceased.
A-yo I shot 'n didn't die. Now
I wanna see who's next to try, 'cause
In my criminal mind no-body violates
The "Don." Y do mothaz let their kids
Out in the street of chalk. They puttin'
"Hitz" on politicians, even cops -
Maybe my ambition to hussle 'n to survive
My pain got me buggin'…After 4 hardcore
Years I still can't quit thuggin'! Where is
The love?

My momma asked me y I do what
I do the way I do it…I didn't answer 'cause
Of the tears that came down from her eyes!
But it will always remain the same 'cause
Of my attitude to thug! My pain gets to me.
Backflashes of Niggaz drownin' in their own blood!
At that time I had my mind full of demons.
I was used to solvin' my problems wit' a click
Of my semi…Now they have me sleepin' wit' my
Infra-red beamz. I hold the scar that shows
J.J. was at war - Come take my body God…

Tupac said to smokje a pound of marijuana, so
I know it ain't long… We went from brothaz and
Sistaz to nigger bitches. I went from No Body
Nigga to the Big Man on the Block! having my
Gat cocked back. but yet ready to die…
Back then, for money, I would've had your
Enemies buried! I know I'm goin' to Hell,
For my sins are too hard to compare!
So all I do is write and talk to my
Troublesome souljas about me and my life, tryin'
To steer 'em away from the Game… All I have
Is my misery…always wantin' revenge for the
Agony the streets gave me! I was in hell, locked
Up in a cell. So now I run from the death makin".
My enemies think I'm dead…Last time I heard
I had 5 in the chest wit' 2 to the head.
Now I laugh and wonda' y did I live the way
I did?! So just take what I say and analyze it…
Get away from the streets 'n love your life…So
I would end this wit' a Question 'How does it feel to
Lose your life over somethin' u did as a kid!'

JONATHAN MALDONADO

WHY I'M HERE

I'm here to learn from
beautiful things
The trees
The flowers
The water
The power
The brightfulness of beauty
The light of nature and
the stature of trees
bring me joy from the earth
The flowers have the power
to bring away any curse
The smell brings romanticism
to my life
because everything
is so beautiful in my sight
I live with flowers
I will die with flowers
And those will be the years
with my strength, my power.

WHY I WRITE

I write because it relieves
my pain
It pulls me away from the
World

Writing brings me to my own universe
full of words for me to think of
My words are the stars,
They twinkle.

My writing
It's like the moon, it brightens
It's like the sun, it's hot
And it's like the world, hateful

I write because to me
words that I write are life
and that life that I bring gives me
more energy to
write, write, write, write and write

KRISTINA MASSA

Getting healed

It's crazy, how a perso
the advantages by, bre
ing up? (say slowly).
So, here comes the sou
the peal, that's pealin
simultaneously, give
tons of loud pealed s
By I everyday shower
Being hereby, as I will
get vanquished near
keeping my eye on you
franchising on amendm
send for more blotter
You been greedy, running
and not even getting
greeted
So, why keep gatherin
All these non-senses,
repeating or it alway
repeated

MANUEL MURRAY

APRIL 1

April 1
Not a day for laughter
But
Just a day and a year
When I will always be serious
About
It's a long story about
April Fool's Day
Turning into April dark Day

It started April 1, 2002
Sunny day when I lost a great friend

It started April 1, 2003
Sunny day when we cry and mourn
Because we miss the one we lost

It started April 1, 2004
Rainy day when we only drink
And cry for the one we lost

But it's just that day when I meet someone
Someone who needs all the help she can get
So now
I look at her and feel committed to her
To be there for her
To not let happen to her and her family
What happened to me

Wake up
Wake up
Be strong and pray
These are things I tell her
But
I don't think she can hear me
But I try
I try to close up that April 1
That keeps on haunting me
Please help me free you from that trap
And you pull me
Out of this April horror.

THIN STRING

Sometimes I think what to do.
Is my life going to be like theirs?
All my life I held back watching people die.
For what?
For nothing.
It's like god holds me back
by a thin string.
I have dreams, in other words, nightmares.
I wake up, middle of the night, scared,
With scars on my body,
Gun in my hand,
Drugs in my pocket,
And I run.
I have dreams.
Yeah.
I have real dreams of becoming
A great human being
A great father
A great husband
A great brother
And a strong, smart man.
Everyday I feel like I'm one step closer
To becoming the man my father was,
And I don't want that. I want to be a man.
I want to be my own man.
I'm sick and I'm tired of people telling me
What I should be
What I should do
What I should know
Where I should go.
I'm gonna make it on my own.
You know why?
Because I don't need you
Or anybody else!

OR DO I?

I just don't want to be like them
Or like my father.
You know, selling drugs
Stealing and killing.
But no
That's just not me.
Some people say
I have the smarts and that
I have the character and that
I have the potential and that
I have the looks.
I don't need to put you through this.
You know.
Remember those dreams we had
Of getting out of the hood
Going to college,
Playing football,
Maybe someday
making it with the big ones.
And after that,
Starting new dreams.

But that don't matter.

Until that day,
God will hold me back
By that thin string.

MANUEL MURRAY

getting healed,
It's crazy!, how a perso
the advantages by, bre
ing up? (say slowly).
so, here comes the sou
the peal, that's pealin
simultaneously, give
tons of loud pealed, s
by ⅞ everyday shower
being hereby, as I will
get vanquished near
keeping my eye on yo
franchising on amendm
send for more blotter
you been greedy, running
and not even getting
greeted
so, why keep gatherin
All these non-senses
repeating, or it alway
repeated

ANTHONY PITTMAN

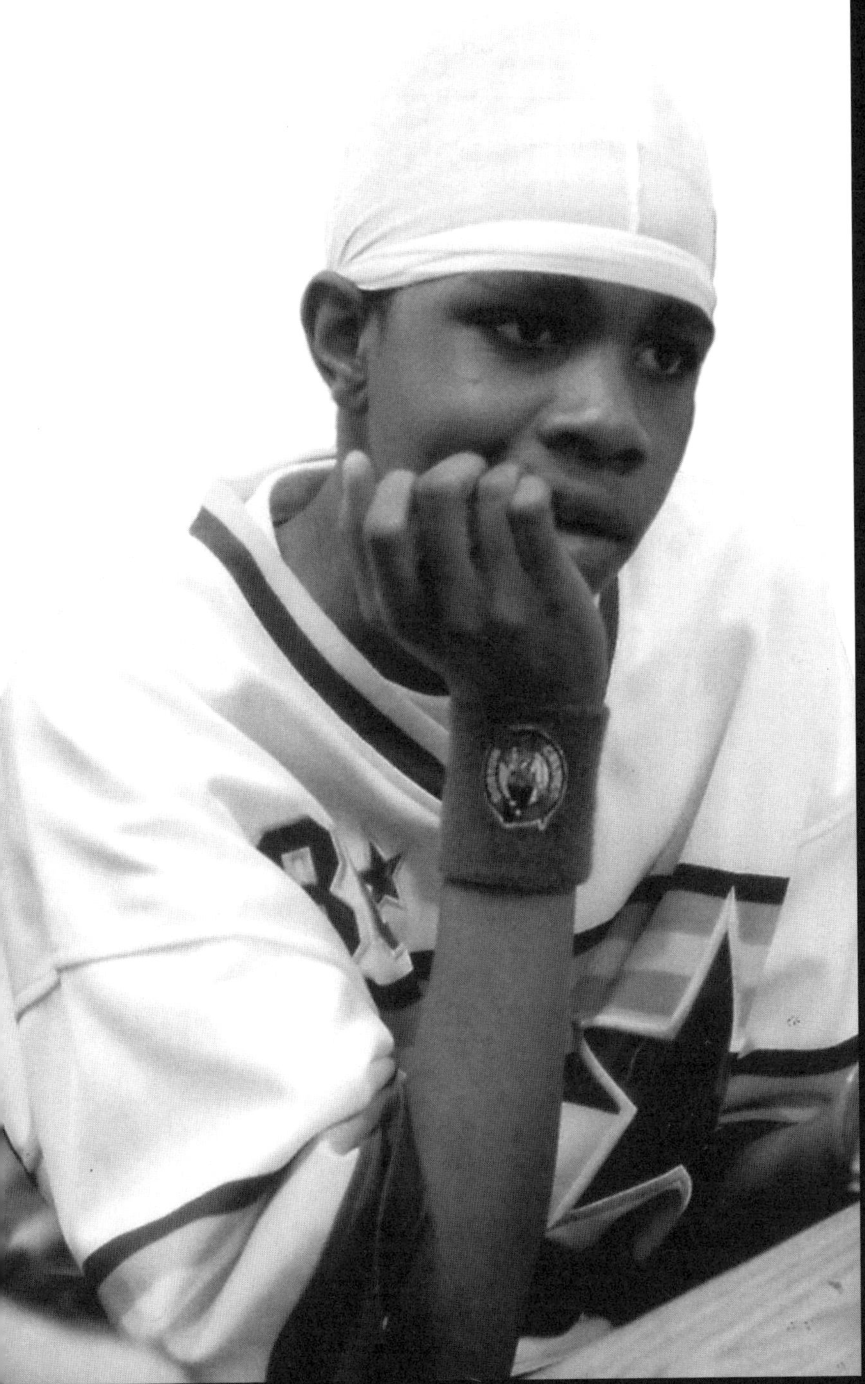

WHAT ARE MY FEELINGS ABOUT RACE?

Racism, racial profiling, racial hatred. Hate is like a hot knife cutting through a stick of butter, doing nothing other than dividing the different shades, languages, accents and features. I feel I should neither love or hate, discriminate or congratulate those who hate the other race just because he thinks they are not worth a thought. But the reality is the other race doesn't think at all, well they don't think of you. At least they think about war and peace. How to survive on the street, how they're going to eat, if their house has heat. You're so far away from their thoughts they could barely think of you. But as a race walks past you glare and you gasp and desperately grasp for your bag. So you're forced into this half life state, blinded by your hate, so you don't see a person, all you see is race. Racism, racial profiling, racial hatred. Hate is like a child's toy paid attention to but there's no reason for it but to make you feel better. But like a child's toy sooner or later it should be forgotten.

CAUSE JOE WANTED TO KNOW WHY

Why I write
Why I write
Why I write…
To express and suppress
Certain images and feelings that
Cannot be understood by the people
Who don't understand why I'm loud, vulgar.
I am who I am.
Why I write
Why I write
Why I write…
To break the chains that remain
Only so that I can look insane.
To have shadows watch and explain
He cannot survive in this world so he must
Remain in a domain that will do nothing
But help him gain nothing but
Unaccomplished dreams
Why I write
Why I write
Why I write…
I write for that young boy
That hooked up with
That young girl and made a young one.
So the process of babies having babies
Has evolved to
Babies making maybes
And that's the only way they know because
These babies having babies
Who evolved into babies having maybes
Will not know how to write unless I write
And show them the light
At the end of the tunnel of ignorance.

Why I write
Why I write
Why I write…
I write for the wrong, the right
The black, the white,
Those who only reach for the things in sight.
So I write, I write, I write.
I write for the children
I write about the killing
I write for that real love
Because everything isn't
lollipops and gumdrops and not either pop,
cops or get shot.
No it's not! 'Cause somewhere
Over the rainbow…is a dream,
A dream that cannot be seen by the people
Who do not understand who I am
Because I am not meant to remain
In this domain.
And these babies having maybes can wrap it up…
If they were taught…

Why I write, why I write, why I write?
It depends on which reason you want.

DAILY ROUTINE

An incipient relationship.
Shiquan an' Sharice.
Both very much in love.
Both very much confused.
Both very predictable.
Both born in a public hospital
Both brought home on public transportation
Raised in public housing
Dropped out of public schools
And now on public aid
Now they live in a land of grim hysteria
The land called Bronx
They both work in a place where they are daily patronized
And don't even realize it
They come home to arguments
Mental and physical abuse
They've been robbed 7 times
Been to jail twice as many times as they were robbed
Combined, they were shot 3 and shot at 11
2 children that are forced to eat mayonnaise sandwiches
and their beverage of choice is tap water with sugar
At least with the odd color of the water
the children can pretend their drink is tea
They must fight with rats and roaches
over who gets to eat the moldy Western Beef bread.
Shariffe and Narika could have a decent meal
If mommy and daddy didn't blow their salary,
Whose figures make the pay seem like an allowance,
On their daily fix
Young Shariffe is HIV positive,
But without insurance he can't get the right heath care.
So what are mommy and daddy supposed to do?
They don't know and they don't care.
So they lay their children down to dream
Because these events have become a daily routine.

WHERE I STAND

Drip
Drip
Drip
The continuous dripping
of the shower I hear
Not very far from where
we are heart to heart
laying near each other,
bare body and bare mind,
not twenty minutes from a time just passed,
when you and I were entwined
and experienced the experience
that made you understand
why you are mine, why I am yours.
Here I am drinking out of this clear glass
Which contains Satan's juice
And I'm sitting bare assed
just staring at you and the continuous
drip drop
drip drop of the shower
and the annoying
tick tock
tick tock
from the clock
floods my brain as I
try to contemplate
the reasons why do you and I
have these great levels of love that we share.
Why do I care about a woman who can't love?
Who can't show affection?
A woman who can't and won't
expose herself emotionally,
but who will still envy the next bitch
who will give me the next kiss on my cheek?
And what's funny is
I see you in the halls and you act

As if I'm not there at all and you went
From every day calling
to not calling me at all,
but you call me your man.
But you do not understand these words,
So why do you speak?
And since we're on the subject,
Why when I go for a kiss
Do you give me the cheek?
And when I talk to that next bitch
Who will give me that next kiss
You look at me like I'm doing something wrong?

And throughout the drip drops
And the tick tocks
My thoughts become a song.
"I don't wanna know if you're playing me
Keep it on the low."
But a voice in my head cries
"Fuck that! Keep it on the high!"
cause I know I want to know
the guy she's sucking
or fucking
so I could put my left foot in her ass and his ass.
See, I know I can overreact
but the fact is
I just can't feel like that.
I shed a tear out of one eye as I just stare
Because I tried to end you and me
But every time I realized that my feeling for you multiplies
But only the love, never the hate
Because the hate only deteriorates
But the reality of the situation is
I just want to say
FUCK YOU! PACK YOUR SHIT AND BOUNCE!

getting healed.
It's crazy, how a pers
the advantages by, 'br
ing up' (say slowly).
So, here comes the sou
the peal, that's pealin
Simultaneously, give
tons of loud pealed, s
By I everyday shower
Being hereby, as I will
get vanquished near
Keeping my eye on yo
franchising on amendm
send for more blotter
You been greedy, running
and not even getting
greeted
So, why keep gatherin
All these non-senses,
repeating or it alway
repeated.

DANIELLE POLLARD

WHITE GOLD

The sun stings their skin as they are hunched over picking this white gold. Long massive sacks dragged behind them. Wide fields of white as far the eye could see. Dark molasses colored men in the brightest of white, the sun stinging their skin as they are hunched over picking this white gold. As the thorns from this white gold tear at their flesh there is a dark red mass lying in the field. Women cry as they look away and work. The body is left lying face down to be a warning, exhaustion does not exist. The white man in the blackest of black hangs his whip dripping with blood as red as a rose from the large red mass that picked his white gold to make his black garments.

The red mass with a name not his own, but given to him in the steps of oppression. This red mass that was forced to forget the language of his people and made to believe the songs he sings about his homeland, his people, his freedom to be of heathen nature. This red mass that all saw as crazy because he spoke of something called Freedom. But you see, this red mass knew someday he would hear the songs of West Africa, his homeland.

He knew his way out.

"No massa, I ain't gonna pick no mo" with every crack of the whip this red mass was closer to his homeland. He smiled as the light faded and his soul rose. He found his Freedom.

YOU DON'T CARE

Deep in my heart I want to die in the pits of hell. I've been shown by those closest to me, those I trust, those holier than thou mother fuckers that that's all I deserve. Fuck, they all see what's wrong with me. My smart fucking mouth, my bad temper, my lazy behavior, my hanging out habits. That's all they see. Shit. Then they have the nerve to act as if they are open minded. Then they throw all my faults and screw ups in my face. I know what I do is wrong, but I can't stop. I scream out for help. No one sees or chooses to answer my cries. What hurts is to have everything I do twisted into something wrong and dirty, or to be told that I need credibility to want to end my life. What the fuck is that? Don't they see what THE...? Oh never mind. My life is worthless as it's always been.

I KNOW HE'S CHANGED

That night he ran from the cops
That night he told me of his numerous felony charges
That night he pulled out his gun
That night they hit him
That night he laughed as they put the cuffs on
That night he made 2g's on the street
That night he got shot
That night he saw me in tears as I saw him
behind those bars
That night he saw me beg just to talk to him
That night I broke every rule just to be with him
That night he told me to give up on him
just like everyone else
That night I stuck by him
That night when I said "I love you"
and he knew I meant it
That night he held me as I cried
That night he ran to me
That night he defended me
That night when nothing else mattered
That night he yelled at me for making my mom worry
That night he stayed off the street and stayed with me
That night he shook me for putting myself down
That night he said all charges were dropped
That night he asked for my help
That night he said he missed me
That night he said he's going back to school
That night my mom said she was proud of him
That night he told me he loved me
That night I knew he's changed

LOVE LOST

All I want is to be loved by you
Growing up being loved by
One woman, that Goddess who
Watched over me and loved me with all my quirks…

This love I destroyed.

Having friends who cared for me
Like brothers and sisters who
Would die for me if it were needed, how lucky…

But this love I destroyed.

I had someone amazing
My king
The one who made me feel like I was worth something?
The one who truly cared…

But you see, I could never love him
I could never love any man

And to you, the only man I need to love me,
Who denies my very existence?

And to you I bid happy Father's Day

DANIELLE POLLARD

getting healed,
It's crazy, how a pers
the advantages by; bre
ing ⬛ up? (say slowly).
So, here comes the sou
the peal, that's pealin,
Simultaneously, give
tons of loud pealed, s
By ⅂ everyday shower
Being hereby, as I will
get vanquished near
Keeping my eye on yo
franchising an amendm
send for more blotter
You been greedy, running
and not even getting
greeted
So, why keep gatherin
All these Non-senses,
repeating, or it alwa
repeated

CATALINA PUENTE

BEEF

Everything is shaking
Everything is breaking
Everyone is yelling
Everyone is sweating
Hits are swung
All the trouble had begun
All the "he said…she said"
That you said, that I said
That he's a dick
That she's a bitch
That you're a liar.
That I'm worth a dollar

Man stop!!!

Silence broke down
Things stopped shaking
Things stopped breaking
Everyone was as quiet as a mute button
Everyone was still as a statue
The she said he's a dick
The he said she's a bitch
The I said you're a liar
The you said I'm worth a dollar
Shit stopped
The beef disturbance finished
My life continued

Too bad…I woke up
Let's start over

CATALINA PUENTE

DEAR...

Poetry, what do you want from me?
Is it the pain inside
Or the rain of the tears I cry?
Poetry, my soul

WRITING VS. WRITING

I want my writing to be heard
Heard loud
Yelled
Screamed
Roared
Special
Sounds + words = meanings
     1. love 2. affection 3. noises
I want my writing to be said
Heard, listened to
     ➢ My writing
     ➢ My writing writing
I want my writing to be put up
To be read = heard
On a radio = heard
In a store, read
A house, read
A bathroom, read
A kitchen, heard
Hallways, heard
A school, read & heard
Train station   Both
Standing   Both
Sitting Running Walking

I want my writing to be famous
Down up
Chewed up
Spit up
Eaten up
Hell no!
Never that!
I want my writing to be treated with respect
Love honor satisfaction
"I can't get no satisfaction" (sing this line out loud)

I want my writing to seen everywhere everywhere
Wow
I can't wait
My writing is beautiful
Yup
I want my writing on a wall
In a book
Newspaper
Everywhere.

YARI

I'm struggling in a world full of hate
The world in my eyes is the color of haze
There are no words I can use to explain
All the hate in my veins
Yet I'm still struggling all the way
The pain and sorrow I simply cannot say
My life, my fears, I don't want to hear
I want to speak loud
Scream at the top of my lungs
But my neck is hung
My voice is mute
I'm thinking and waiting
I want to cry but I can't
It's so hard to explain the story of a girl
A girl full of struggles
In her heart is an arrow
An arrow of hate
An arrow of love
The hate in her heart is cutting through
As she cries to heal the wounds
Of all the hate and sorrow
Thrust deep in her veins
She cries immortally in a house full of pain
There's rage in her veins
Hate in her blood
Love in her heart
Is all she has
I can see her clearly
Her eyes, her tears
I can see her through the mirror of fears
Yet she's still struggling all the way
Down a never ending brick road

YARITZA RODRIGUEZ

LOVE YOURSELF MORE

I didn't understand the fact that when they said I couldn't see my son Dacity anymore. They tried and tried to make it clear, but I guess that I wanted him so much I was in denial. Kris didn't like him much, but I needed Kris in my life. I couldn't live without him. Kris was an excellent boyfriend, you know, when he wasn't drunk or high…but he looked so cute when he was asleep afterwards. He treated me good, except for the times I act up and he "puts me in my place". He says that I'm a lady and I "should do all what ladies do". I was pregnant when I met Kris and he named my son for me, he named him Dacity because he said I had the audacity to keep him. Kris never liked him very much and he always left those things lying around. Dacity kept crying so I went out for some juice and when I returned I saw Dacity fast asleep, although I thought that his drool looked kind of thick. He'd been asleep 3 days before I thought something was wrong. I had been so high with Kris that I forgot all about Dacity. I took him to the doctor and they said he was sleeping in the way he was before he came to earth. Kris got mad when the guys in blue put on a pair of locked silver bracelets on him. He said I would get a pair too. I just walked around and around my new apartment. I thought it was very nice, you could sleep anywhere you wanted 'cause the floor was very soft, padded. I asked them to put a crib in here for Dacity, but they said he was still asleep. It has been three years of unending dreams. When will my baby wake up?

ALL ME

Dedicated to all girls that think their outer beauty is
more important than their inner gold.

Long black hair
Chinese eyes
Light tan skin
An hourglass shape
Is what most people see
Well.. what people don't see is that I,
As a person, need attention
In all other ways their appearance.
Shit!
When you look at me you wouldn't think
That I
Love poetry, dance, music, art, fashion and school
No!
People don't fuckin' look at that
All they worry about is if I bend over
Will they see what color thong I'm wearing today
They don't see the passion in my heart
Or the knowledge in my brain
All they see is the
Long black hair
The Chinese eyes
The light tan skin
And the hourglass shape
The physical appearance isn't important
As long as you have the heart of gold
And the mind to go with it
That's all that matters.
So if I shave my head bald
Get a tan
Wear glasses
Don't give a fuck what no one thinks

Of me and
I gain a few pounds
Would you still see the person you saw before?
No?
Well I kind of expected that
But
You know what?
I didn't give a fuck from the start
'cause you don't have a say
in how I see myself.
I know who I see in the mirror
And if all you see is the
Long black hair
Chinese eyes
Light tan skin
And an hourglass shape
Then you've surely missed out.

DEAR GOD

The pain I endured is unexplainable
Unimaginable to those who haven't felt it
Unknowing of the risk she took
'cause no one told you
unthought of the decisions she
then would have to make
if only she knew of the tears
she would cry
why am I gaining weight?
why am I feeling the way I feel?
why when I told you did you beat me so?
You said that you loved me
And that together we would grow
You said you didn't want me
You said you wanted me dead
You said those things to me I put the
Gun to my head
But in all that confusion
And in all the mist
I felt the tender nudge of my unborn
Kick
Then I thought of you and all the lies
You told me
I thought of my baby first
I didn't want this but this is the life
I chose
You will never have to see me as far as
You should know
'cause I'm having my baby not for you
but for me
I want you to die for all the pain
You've caused me
My baby and I will live our lives
'cause I'm not who you thought

I was
I won't live through your eyes
This is your child
You can either love him or leave him
Yes! It's a boy
your son your legacy
in the new world he will live in
with or without the guidance of his father
the man you could show him to be
I guess I'll be mommy and daddy
But even if you don't want to be there
I will find him a daddy who will care.

FANTASY & REALITY

Dear Journal

The steam is rising, filling all the space in the bathroom, sign of the hottest water you've bathed in for a long time. You feel as refreshed as you ever have. As you leave the bathroom you fall into the warm embrace of your mother as she hugs you and kisses you on your forehead with her cherry lip balm that you gave on her birthday a year ago and she still wears to show how much she appreciates the gift. She says "good morning, lovely child" and shows you to a seat at the dining table, the table where you sit every morning and night and eat meals as a family. You finish eating your healthy, warm breakfast and thank your mother as you're about to leave for school. You grab another warm embrace as your mother tells you she loves you very much and with that smile from ears to asshole you awake to the bitches and bastards your mother is calling your sister and the hard bagels being slammed into the toaster. The darkness of early morning and the coldness of my sheets run a chill up my spine. I get up and my feet touch the cold floor, stepping over broken toys and dirty clothes as I go to the bathroom, and like every morning there's no hot water. I'm dressed and step out of my own hell and step into another where you see constant poverty, violence and illiteracy. No! But do we have a choice? Hell no! Can we make it better? Yes. But do we? NO! So what do we have? NOTHING! Only until we make the change.

WHAT IT IS TO WRITE

Finally
Today is Friday
I get to relieve myself
Relieve myself of heartaches and headaches
And all other emotions felt during the week
Putting my pen to my paper letting my problems go
Gives me a sense of relief from what was a torturous week
Allowing my body to take in all of nothing
At least for 3 periods 1 day a week
Writing my emotions down for my review
Later on in my life will allow me to see my progress
Through this life.

HEIDE

No need to front for me
I already know who you really are
No need to front for me, there really is no need
There's really no need to deny me love anymore
I will no longer ask for it
Although it is something I desperately need
I'll no longer taunt you with my asking for an
"I love you" or a hug and kiss.
You don't have to front
Front like you love me when you're with your friend to
make yourself look like the caring and concerned mother
When you're not
Instead of instilling a loving and caring environment for
your children to grow up in you create one that is filled
with fear instead of respect
and abuse instead of love.
You just don't have to front.
They say that Madre es una
There's only one mother but if a mother should do what
you do
I'd rather not have a mother at all.
Other mothers calm their child whenever they're scared
She supposed to wipe your tears whenever you cry
Why didn't you know that you are the most important
person in my life?
Why don't you love me like you used to?
You hurt me on a daily basis,
like it's on your list, how to make me hurt.
I hate the fact that every day I yearn for your love
and every day you deny me it.
I hate the fact that the only love that I get is from the
man that I love,

Or do you even know who that is
I hate the fact that I go to sleep waiting for you to wish
me a good night.
I hate the fact that my love is fading by the minute
But I'll tell you one thing, now that this is off my chest
You no longer have to front.

MY MOTHER'S CHILD

I'm 16 years old
The B.X being my life
Living here and becoming the B.X
16 years of being my mother's child
But not being a child at all
I, standing on my own two feet
Ready to face the world alone
With the knowledge in my brain
And the power of my fists
With that advantage at hand
Becoming a woman I will at last
Open my eyes to all new things
To love, anger, and all different feelings
I will to my feeling no longer be in denial
Cause no matter what
I'll forever be my mother's child

MANANA

My tears are forming a small puddle on the sheets
on which you slept
I'm wailing and sobbing trying to relieve myself of
the pain I feel in my heart
Amar, trying to keep control of me as I lose control
of myself
I felt dead to all other emotions then to the feeling
of pain
Looking at your normally warm, dark skin complexion
turned into an ice cold pale one
Playing with your long black Indian hair as you slept in
your eternal sleep
Holding you as I whispered in your ear for you to open
your eyes just hoping that you would.
Punching the nurse when he said time was up
It was in fact time for me to let you go
Not that I wanted to cause I would never willingly let
you go but…why did you leave me?
Leave me in this world where you know I'm all by myself
I have no one
Why did you leave me, why did you do that to me?
I was mad that you didn't hold on
I was mad at you cause you left me alone
I was mad at the lord for taking you from me
I was mad at myself for being selfish
Selfish enough to want you only for me
For my eyes alone and for no one else to see
To see that true angels do exist and that you were mine
Now you are where you truly belong in the heavens
You're a happy family now
Now you could have the space in you heart filled
It's no longer empty cause you have your family and me
Your heart now is complete
No longer will you have to cry

No longer will I have to cry
Even though I will anyways
I'll love you forever
I'll love you for life
I'll love you till the end of time and until mañana

SHOWTIME @ THE APOLLO

It was the constant
"Visionary, visionary, visionary" flow
that kept the audience entwined
with each word the poet spoke having them
feel what we were saying
It was a time that we
SCREAMED IN THE FACE OF DEFEAT
as we overcame the pain in tears of
heartbreak, loneliness and anger
and psychopathic boyfriends
that make you kill your child
Or are you the psycho that did it?
It was the confusing
"Humm humm humm"
questioning if what he said was worth
questing, making me
ask myself what the fuck
was he humming for?
It was the succession of a
young girl's determination
to succeed at weight loss
that convinced her that every
curve in her body was perfect.
It was Dani's relationship problems
that made her love the lips and eyes
that lied to her and the big hands
and arms that beat her and threw her
across the room.
Or it was just a phase
Hummmm…
It was the energy that we had
representing the school
And congratulations to Dani
representing the Heights

Big props to those people
who made themselves look like a fool
And props to me 'cause I performed
excellently despite needing to pee
the whole night.
It was the Styrofoam cups that
kept us on task
Or was it the long-haired muscle
boy with the nice tight ass?
Well, whatever it was, even if
we explained, y'all wouldn't know
how it felt, how we really felt
that night at the Apollo.

THANK YOU

Needing to love one
Needing them to love me
Gaining a sense of respect for not only myself
Whether you like
White boys
Black bows
Red clothes
Blue clothes
Long hair
Black nails
Spiked collars
No one cares
In this place we're a family
And without this family I wouldn't be here
How do I know this?
Not being able to express ones self could lead
To overwhelming anger and tears
And the fear of not reaching
the expectations of my parents
lead to the flood of decisions in my mind
whether to live or die
do write or wrong
the easiest way out is the quickest decision to make
but to look at my past I see that if I
do that my baby girl will grow up with no
sense of direction
without this family that I have adopted
that has accepted me
I too will be lost
So thank you Roland, Amy and most of all Joe
For opening this door to new light
And thank you all known as my family
For letting me know that my life
Is worth the fight.

GARLIC MUSTARD/TACONIC

The scent of garlic mustard and the sounds of a waterfall give off a very peaceful feeling. Spring is here and love is in the air as I see the true desire in the eyes of my peers. Dodging the sun and the troublesome gnats, just hoping that I could get some relief from the both of them. Anxious to spot my favorite insect, the dragon fly, so that we could become friends and he would protect me forever. Poison ivy and mountain laurel, two highly toxic plants, and yet remain unknown to "hood man." Hoping that when I got home to the Bronx I would get some type of positive response to my wonderful experience but instead I get total ignorance. You, not knowing of such peace, but wanting to go back to the shootouts and the loud Spanish households. I, just hoping it could be the was the way it was at the Taconic. I guess it can't always be. Oh well. I guess I just have to be nature. Nature being me.

KARINA SANCHEZ

getting healed
It's crazy, how a pers
the advantages by, bre
ing up, (say slowly).
So, here comes the sou
the peal, that's pealing
simultaneously, give
tons of loud pealed, $
By # everyday shower
being hereby, as I will
get vanquished near
keeping my eye on yo
franchising on amendm
send for more blotter
You been greedy, running
and not even getting
greeted
So, why keep gatherin
All these non-senses,
repeating or it alway
repeated

DORIAN SANDERS

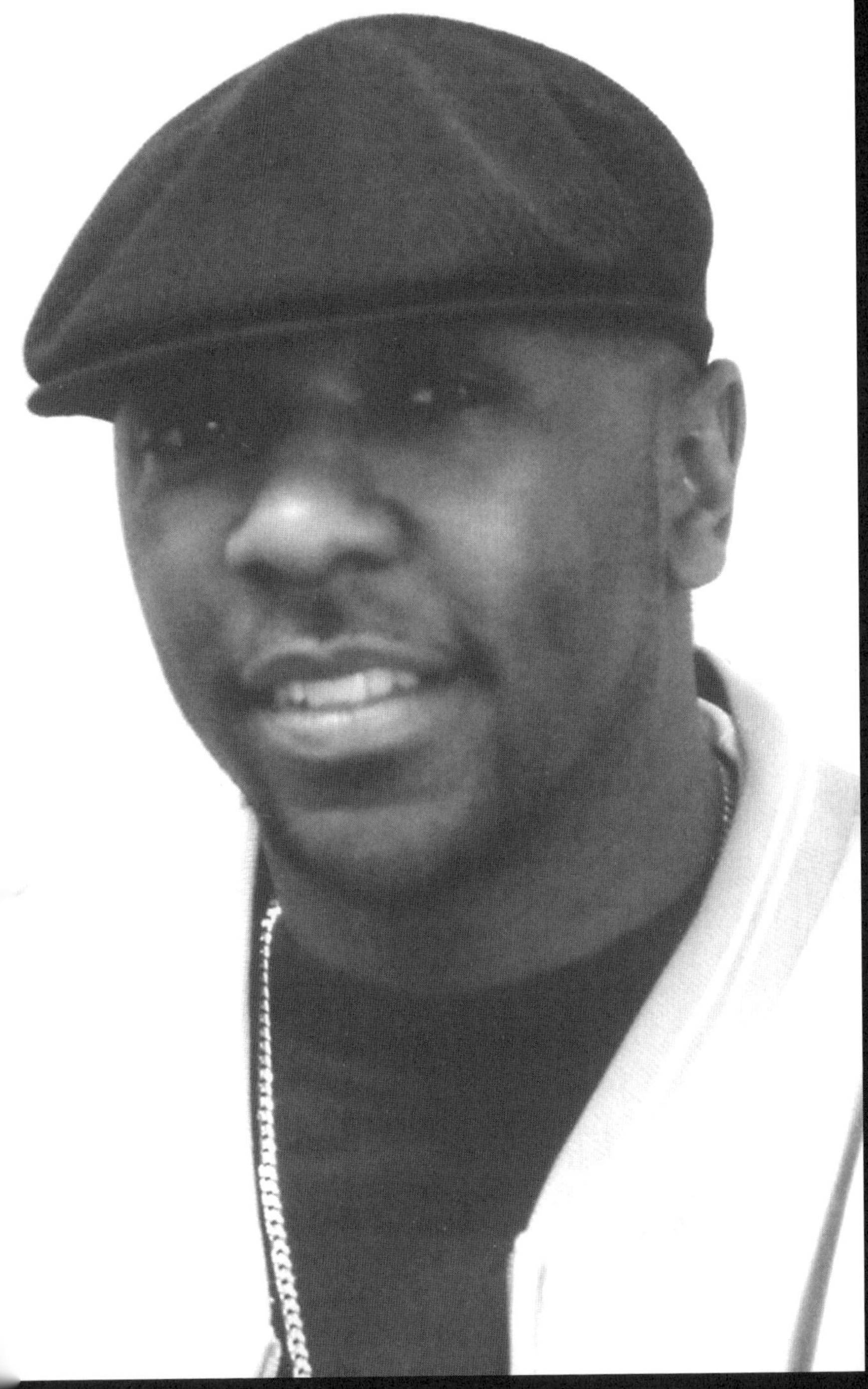

WHY I WRITE...

Try to describe the world out of these eyes of mine
How I see it, what I witnessed, how I live it,
With plans to make it vivid for the outsiders looking in.
Camouflage or blend my thoughts
On the white lines of the paper. Some died for
the paper, some even sniffed white lines of the paper,
damn, it's like I'm getting off the topic, can't stop it.
Just throw away or hide my pen. Don't even need it
cause my mind is flowing 24/7 even when it's sleeping
it's dreaming, 'til I'm called to the heavens

DORIAN SANDERS

MAISHA TULIVU FISHER

IT'S SHOWTIME AT THE APOLLO

It's Showtime at the Apollo
Our youth bare gifts
Wrapped in Truth
Accented by Rhyme
KiKi Shepard weeps at the window
while the sandman is held hostage by their cadence
There won't be any rubbing of the lucky tree stump
Because luck is just another 4-letter word
Replaced with Skill,
Substituted for Purpose
Displaced by Wisdom
Arrested by Integrity
No R&B intermissions with odes to bump and grind
No shots out to name brands whose proceeds will never
be found
In a neighborhood near you
The youth don't stop
Won't stop
Get it Get it
Their lyrics take names and point fingers
Absentee fathers indicted by the ink in their pens
Trespassers of young women's bodies are imprisoned
In between the lines of their journals
With no chance for parole
Brown faces and bodies that won't take their seats
quietly in the colored section
Unless it's by choice
It's Showtime at the Apollo
Our youth bare gifts
Will you
Be
Open
To
Receive

IT WAS ALL GOOD

It was all good when they were only lyrics to a song
But when it became my fate, those words I began to hate
Usher crooning
Girls swooning
And trying to figure out why my 30 something ass is still
humming along
To a Song Ey Hahn so distant
And sadly so near
No visible distinction between my roaring twenties
And shit going on this year
A few degrees later and a parade of letters behind my
name
But issues with niggas still remain the same
No commitment, no promises and no one to have my
back
Thought I was still in junior high when folks didn't know
how to act
It was all good when they were only lyrics to a song
But when it became my fate, those words I began to hate
R. Kelly whining
Young girls shinin'
Him on...
But not enough to put his ass in jail where he belongs
Still bouncing to the thong song
And don't trip he had me steppin' in the name of love
Integrity and self respect somewhere in the back seat of
his jeep
Somewhere between the R & B
I got lost and could not see
My way out...
It was all good when they were only lyrics to a song
But when it became my fate, those words I began to hate
Eminen in Elvis face
You think that shit is funny

Using Black folks style to make some money
But when Eminem got caught on tape
Talking about a Black girl he loved to hate
Not one of my brothers stepped up to the plate
Dre and 50cent still posted up behind him like the FOI
Even though it is my image he sells and folks continue
to buy
It was all good when they were only lyrics to a song
But now that it is my fate
These words I have come to hate
And the song goes on and on…

MAISHA TULIVU FISHER

OE UBILES

TUESDAY NIGHT UPRISING

The sun dives through antique windows into the west
and it's fading light reveals the eyes of young poets
which are filled with the light of true story
they are calling the people to this celebration of life
an act older than writing
and bibles
and Korans
and torahs
and money
their eyes dancing in story's blue light
its fire pushing back the night
Anansi and Bubalah take seats in corners
Coyote wails
Ancient griots with their hands enmeshed in mnemonic
strings glide in and
Out of shadow
Thoth's baboon grin flashes
Unseen, yet witnessing silently
The songs of the young calling and calling and calling
in the voice of gated
Windows and nightmares and hopes and dreams and
dissatisfaction
On the podium an invincible tower of Babel
The real united nations of a just world called to order
Poems like hymns
Like psalms
Like the night lotus unfolding
Like sermons
The poems take flight in the night air and erupt and
re-erupt
From faces unlined by time and minds unscarred by the
cynicism of our
Metallic and

Mercantile now
Word after word line after line in tone after tone
The new ghost dance is mastered
It calls for a new world
That can never be
Until we dream it
Sing it and poem it into being
A world of the free the home of the brave
Literate and enchanted
All clothed in beauty of loves wisdom
For ever
And ever
Be poetry

FORTY SECOND STREET LIBRARY, A JITTERBUG WALTZ

Danced
At the main branch of the ancient tree called
"i wish to know"
The stone lions face outwards
Their mineral eyes
Unseeing
Gazing frozen on the avenues of power without wisdom
Perched on steps as linear as mayan temples roman roads
or
Eight bar blues
Pigeon speckled gods
In the voices of mountains
They call upon us to enter and to learn
The spirits of knowing dwell herein
The healers of hearts
The midwives of minds
The sucklers of ideas
The tricksters and sages of all times and places
From the human story
Whose sounds simply mean
I am
We be
I am we are
Of the people
Enter now
Peacefully
And discover yourselves

FOR KAMAL SINGH, REQUIEM AND LIBATION

Our prayer our dream as always is of change

As in the ancient forms red wine is spilled
Returning to green earth
Our sorrows and our suffering

Kamal we did not know you
Know of your indian/african dooglah passage
Your brown mask among brown masks lining hallways

Your mask missing now
And present only among brown girl masks
With your photo clutched in round brown fists
Eliptic eyes like starlight
Silently weeping

In this school place
Adult masks in all shades of time and place
Dancing slow circles
Bereaved and bewildered how do we how do we how
do we
Teach love sanity safety
With so little of our own

An episcopal shadow lingers
Autopsy reports no more useful than
Liturgy
Ashes to ashes to ashes to ashes to
Dust to dust to dust to dust to
The sounds of gunfire everywhere
Powowowowowowowowowowowpow

If music is the sum of our acquired sounds then what symphony
Is written in the scale of gunfire

How do we stop the war how do we stop the war at home
How do we stop the slow dance of violence
This shuffle into extinction
This avalanche of self hatred
This anomie of teflon bullets
Totems of our disdain for ourselves and for each other

Brain material on the wall, edgecombe ave
Blood clotted into tobacco brown and black stains,
110th st.
La brea la brea the great beasts trapped forever
Who will study our bones when we are ever so long gone?
The guns roar in the anti-language
The mental shroud
The silent sound of silence
Foreshadowing our doom
Change now my people
Change now…………..

JOE UBLIES

AMY OLGA SULTAN

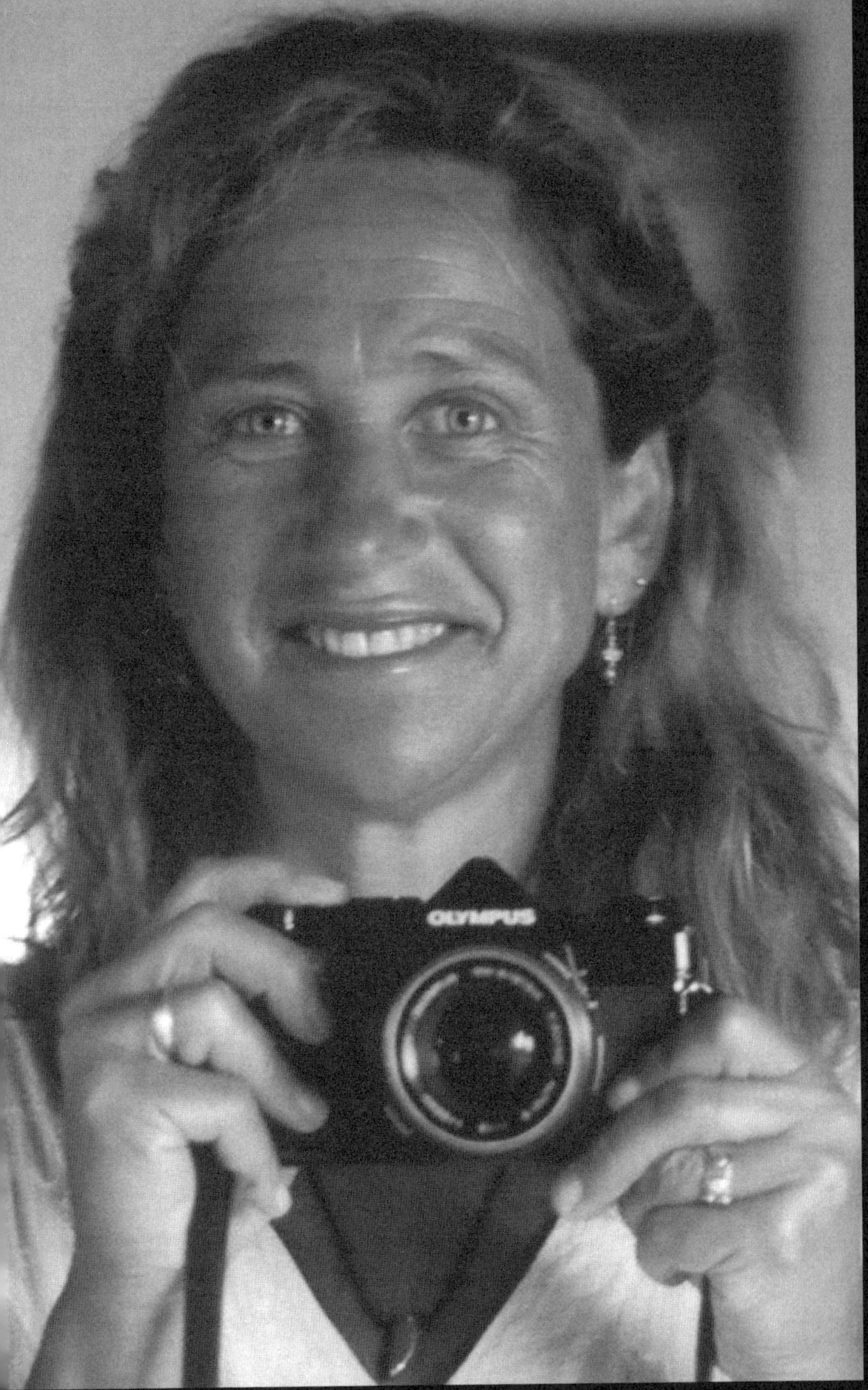

COASTAL EVACUTION ROUTE

Words of magic
words of danger, implied
Coastal
Evacuation
Route

Tides roiling
Tides rising
Sea amok
Sea bezerk
Sea never ending
Ending life as we know it
On the ocean
On the edge
On the cusp of all that means life
and beginning and no limits

Each time I drive past this sign
I inhale and see in my head
The wall of water, never ending
High and higher reaching over the
fragility of sand and grass
Making the end of time seem here
today, now and then again
Never.

The coast has been evacuated before
But the coast, the dune, the beach is here
In my head, in my face, in my heartbeat.

DARK/END

kiss longing to go far
into marrow
longing to fuse.
instead an end
to end the end,
to be left
to be left a vacuum
to wait for your green light
to hold in the rest
to never speak
swallow every meaning
tamp down the spark
keep the flame dead
ignore the fire
tread lightly
do not pass go
stay regular
deny the truth
don't say i love you
don't say anything
don't see what i see
don't.

PUNCTURE THE HOT HEART

Puncture the hot heart
Steal, squelch the air, crab the light
Take everything

A MID WINTER'S NIGHT DREAM

In this, the darkest heart of winter
The time of deepest ice
I want just that you want
What I want
That you will be bountiful
Not stingy
With the knife, with the words
Drawn by the knife
Reaching the soul sinew
Casting words untethered my way
Untamed, unchained,
Release the truth to me, at least that

MY HEAD ACHES

Tectonic plates saw
Back and forth
Uneven and faulty
They grind, rough edges
No smoother with age, now
More uneven, more erose
Make me blind, squinty
I touch my knurled and
Knotty scalp with agitated fingertips
Tapping hard, the base of my skull
Echo of my hard bone head

THE LIGHTS, DECEMBER 2001

I stand at the lip
of the bowl that holds
the keening -
a well of prayer extinguished

The road of light cascades up, now
two flashlights casting up
into a sky - a night, now
that reveals orbs of stars and planets
and moons of those planets are revealed
in the absence of the towers -
as those lights were pulverized -
the white glass of fluorescence gone,
smashed, incinerated with bone
and skin and eyes and lips that were
kissed and cherished and are lost
for all time.

Between these roads of light
each cloudless night - a star or a
constellation holds my eye between the 2 beams -
this path I hope to heaven,
lit like a landing strip
and from where I stand
rooted at the lip of the light
stretches up to a pyramid in the darkness.

peace

MEMORIAL DAY

The rain drove down
As we drove out
Out of the city
Across the Brooklyn Bridge
Frantic with police activity
A ferocity of visible force
Sirens, bomb trucks
Cops leaping from car roofs
To the walkway spanning the river
The walkway of Whitman.

We sit in traffic on the Grand Central Parkway,
Past LaGuardia just as a
Mammoth plane descends just above,
huge, huge plane just above us
Bad for the brain
Bad for muscle memory, cell memory
Deep body memory
Of a roar, then louder roar, then deafening whine
Muted thud, muffled implosion
No breath breathed
All silence, hushed awful silence
All sound voiceless, tongueless
Every voice stricken dumb

A wail, a murmur, a moan
A moan that grows in a collective wail
Of disbelief of what our eyes see
A gaping, fiery hole in the skin of the skyscraper
A woman leaning out of a window just below the fiery
hole
She's waving a white sweater
Seventy stories up in the air

Silence, then the sound of wailing
Sirens, a hundred sirens and a blur of firemen's faces
A parade of faces looking up and out of the windows
Of their trucks, a last look, frightened

I run to find my son, in despair
And then there is another noise,
Percussive boom
The sky is filling with smoke and flame
And I look up at the shattering as I hold onto Sam
We both look up
Holding him to me to keep him from harm
But it is too late
We have looked up to see the whirls of paper
Glass steel ribboned like confetti, swirling upward
Gleaming in the perfection of late summer sun
In the force of this conflagration
We have looked up to see
So many fly off into empty air,
On no wing and no prayer.

In memory.

AFTERWARD

May 2, 2004

Last night, under the 3/4 moon that danced through scudding clouds, I ran across the sand, spinning into a cartwheel, landing in the cold water of the ocean's edge.

This morning I walked miles along the beach – I looked down at my cold feet in the water. My blue glasses were washing in the early tide, just where they must have dropped last night during my reverie. They are covered with salt and slightly sand scratched but the sea returned them to me so that I could see to write this morning.

I haven't walked this beach in over 6 months, the first winter of my life that I haven't made the hejira to soothe myself with the constant roar of wave after wave. Why?

The days of this winter have passed with my head and heart wrapped in the words of the poets that fill this book. I am done with the editing. I have pored over pages of journals entrusted to me. I have read oceans of very sorrowful words, words of pain, some of delight and wonder, but many of unbearable loss. These young rebel voices you find here resound with intrepid resilience, with the miracle of each kid's wild spirit. My dreams go with each one of them, each on the path of a learner, of a true human being.

To all you kids…well, you know. Be bold and sing your story with love, clarity and conviction. Peace out!

AMY OLGA SULTAN

Thank you to everyone who supported me in this work. Eve Banilower, Carla Bauer, Doris Blum, Brenda Bravo, Zoe Caldwell, Kristen Caskey, Jane Glicksman, Jane Kent, Betty Klein, Mitchell Korn, Rain Kramer, Chuck Levey, Lillian Martinez, Jackie Pine, Raun Rasmussen, Barbara Rittberg, Roberta Samet, Michelle Schrieber, Nadia Rasmussen-Schreiber, David Storey, Jack Storey, Randall Wreghitt, Lisa Zabel, Dena Zemsky.

And my deepest love and appreciation to Ed & Sam Sturmer for all of your unwavering patience with my absorption in this amazing journey.

Roland & Joe, mi companeros. Gracias!~Viva!

getting heated,
Its crazy, how a pers
the advantages by; bre
ing [illegible] up; (say slowly).
so, here comes the sou
the peal, that's pealing
simultaneously, give
tons of loud pealed, [illegible]
By I everyday shower
Being hereby, as I will
get vanquished near
keeping my eye on yo
franchising an amendm
send for more blotter
You been greedy, running
and not even getting
greeted
So, why keep gatherin
All these Non-senses,
repeating or it always
repeated,

thing healed. WH
ts crazy, how a person
he advantages by, brew
g up? (say slowly).
here comes the sounds
epeal, that's pealing o
multaneously, give ou
ns of loud pealed, mor
everyday showerin
ing hereby, as I will no
et vanquished nearli
eeping my eye on you,
anchising an amendmen
end for more blottering
been greedy, running a
d not even getting th
reeted
why keep gathering,
ll these Non-senses, yo
peating or it always
repeated.